The Doctor as Customer

The Revised and Expanded 3rd Edition

Andy Farah MD

The Doctor as Customer
A Guide for Pharmaceutical Representatives
Copyright © 1999
Andy Farah, M.D.

The revised 2nd edition 2000
The revised 3rd edition 2004

ISBN: 0-9678437-2-3

Library of Congress
Control Number: 2004095508

Printed in the United States by:
Battleground Printing and Publishing
3712 Old Battleground Rd.
Greensboro, NC 27410
1-336-288-6325

Acknowledgements

The outstanding representatives who inspired this book are too numerous to thank properly in this limited space. It is simply best to tell you that when I reflect on how you do your job, I am inspired to take my skills to a higher level as well. I also wish to thank Gayle Smith-Neely, Matthew Bee, Mike, Leah, Dylan, and Q for their continuing support.

This book is dedicated to Marilyn Farah,
1930 – 1992.

Contents

Introduction

Part I – Your Customer

1. Medical Training-What you need to know........................1
2. The Basics of Medical Decision Making........................11
3. The Psychology Behind Prescription Choices..................19
4. The Three Main Influences on Prescription Habits............29

Part II – The Art of Medical Selling

5. Rep Basics..39
6. Customer Expectations..43
7. The Essential Elements of the Detail...........................49
8. The Top Ten Obstacles to Getting Your Message Out.........57
9. Relationship-Based Selling.......................................73
10. The Comfort Zone (of Prescribing).............................79
11. The Close...85
12. What REALLY Changes Prescription Habits..................89
13. The Top Mistakes that Reduce Market Share.................95

Part III – The Next Level

14. The VALUE Mindset..109
15. Bringing Value to Every Call...............................113
16. Get Invited Back..117
17. The Speaker Program and Physician Education.............121

Glossary of Essential Information................................131
Contact Information...137
Seminar Information..138

Introduction

Mission Impossible...

Each pharmaceutical representative has been assigned an impossible mission. He or she must navigate a psychological obstacle course through 'access guardians' in order to get quality time with physicians – then, build rapport and educate each physician about one or more products, address all questions and concerns about usage, and finally, accomplish the elusive 'close of the sale.' You may have less than thirty seconds to achieve the ultimate goal: to reach that point where the physician feels completely comfortable prescribing your products when indicated. If you truly succeed in your mission, you will have made a lasting impact, and your customers will remember your information as they go through their days, mindful of opportunities to help patients with your products.

Many of you identified with this career description seven years ago in the first edition of *The Doctor as Customer* – assuring me that you set out daily on a mission with plenty of obstacles, betrayals, and unexpected twists. Further, since the publication of the first edition, we have seen numerous launches of excellent products, thousands of new representatives competing for the same small slice of time, the introduction of 'pharma guidelines,' and prescription drug coverage has, at various times, taken center stage in the political arena.

As these factors have increased the complexity of the landscape, your mission has grown even more challenging.

And, as you have experienced, just *completing* the mission is often not good enough. The vast majority of representatives are capable of this feat, difficult as it is. You are highly trained and skilled professionals, just like your customers, so it is no surprise that there are thousands of outstanding representatives out there every day achieving quality time and using it to educate physicians. To truly complete your mission and have a meaningful and lasting impact, you must stand out.

When I speak to representatives in training, through teleconferences, or coach them individually, this one question is asked more frequently than any other: 'How can I stand out among so many excellent reps?'

The new edition of *The Doctor as Customer* will focus on these two areas:

1. The basics of becoming an excellent representative, and
2. Standing out among other excellent representatives.

Part I explores your customers: how we are trained, the basics of medical decision-making, and the psychology of prescription patterns. After all, you have to understand how the customer is thinking in order to change prescribing habits. Part II will focus on the art of medical detailing, and cover topics such as the 'close of the sale' and the most common mistakes made by reps. Part III will inspire you to take your physician interactions to the next level and bring real value to every call you make. In this section, you will learn how a solid relationship can transform you into a welcomed and valuable member of the treatment team, not just another person competing for limited time.

The glossary of essential information covers topics every rep should know, such as the schedule system of controlled drugs, pregnancy ratings, and how to interpret the most important statistical measures in medical research.

Sure, there are thousands of representatives, and it may seem that some days the majority of them are in your territory, competing for your slice of time, but there is always time for the best.

And yes, there are more products in every class, and the numbers will keep expanding – but each medication has unique advantages, so your role as the front-line educator is even more important.

There have always been external forces imposing limits on your ability to get the message out, but you were hired because of your skills, which include the creativity you need to overcome barriers.

The mission is indeed challenging, and may seem impossible at times, but your contributions to health care in your community are too important for you to allow any of these factors to defeat your message.

If you have questions that are not answered in this book, please email them to:

drandyfarah@yahoo.com

Best of luck - and read on!

Paradigm Shift

If I need a new car, I see a salesperson. If I need information to support patient care, I listen to skilled and highly trained professional representatives. The term 'sales-rep' is a disservice, and diminishes the reality of who you are: a health care educator.

Just as you strive to speak accurately about your products, strive for that same accuracy in terms of your career description. We consider you as providers of patient and professional support and ongoing medical education. Perhaps in the near future you will be part of the re-named 'Medical Education Division.'

Part 1

Your Customer

Doctors and nurses have chosen a helping profession, and spend our lives in service to others, but who serves our needs? Who can we rely on for support in our mission? The pharmaceutical industry and its representatives have been there for us for over a century - imagine how little we could offer patients without them.
Kitty Stafford RN

Chapter 1

Medical Training –
What You Need to Know

It is important to know where your customers come from. An understanding of the specialized training we receive will also help you understand the process of medical decision making – specifically what goes into the process of choosing the right prescription for each patient.

The first two years of medical school include courses on anatomy, neuroanatomy, physiology, biochemistry, genetics, embryology, pharmacology, pathology, immunology, microbiology, and behavioral sciences. There are also courses that teach the art of clinical reasoning, and even some exposure to patient care.

Clinical Reasoning courses are all about thinking like a doctor, and if there is one theme, it is best summarized as 'when someone is sick, consider every possible cause!' A typical format for these classes involves reading assignments on clinical problems and then meeting for group discussions. The clinical problem may be simple, such as a cough, or fever, or it may be a more complex example, like vertigo after a head injury. As more details of the cases are revealed, the students discuss what they would test for, and what diagnoses to consider. The leader of the group is an attending physician with plenty of clinical experience. Their goal is to guide the art of thinking about how to evaluate a patient. In general, they make sure we focus on listening to the patient and getting a good history of the illness, and then consider every possible cause of their complaints - a patient with a headache could be under psychological stress, or they may have a brain tumor. We are trained to ask the right questions and do the right workup so every cause is ruled in or out.

During the first two years the attrition rate is about 10-20%, meaning one or two of every ten students will drop out at some point. These years are definitely stressful, as the amount of information to memorize and process can be quite overwhelming. One of my close friends, George, was a particularly bad influence then. As you know from your own experiences, two people can become close because their names are next to each other in an alphabetized list and they are always assigned to work together. As we shared dissecting duties one long summer, I learned that George had the amazing ability to spend the weekend before exams in Cancun with his girlfriend and still score higher than ninety-five percent of the class on all of them. I tried to emulate his study habits, but after the first series of exams I realized I'd need to study about ten hours to his every one!

After these fun filled years of battling sleep in lecture halls, dissecting cadavers, and looking at exciting pathology slides, we take part I of the National Medical Boards. This is a two-day affair that despite how much time we study (or spend on the beaches of Mexico), remains very challenging. Because it is written by the top researchers in the basic sciences, it often includes terminology that we encounter for the first time on the exam itself! Students must pass in order to advance to the third year, and most schools will allow a second examination the following year for those who need another try.

The third year of medical school involves clinical rotations, and at last you find yourself in the wards and outpatient clinics meeting patients. Each student rotates through internal medicine, cardiology, obstetrics, pediatrics, surgery, and psychiatry. On some rotations you are given the authority to manage a great deal of the patient care. It depends, of course, on the setting and number of residents supervising your group. At the end of each rotation, you take an exam (called a 'Mini-Board') related to that specialty and are assigned both subjective and objective grades.

I started in obstetrics, a busy and generally student-unfriendly department at my school. It was a high-volume service, and as a student I delivered several infants with the resident looking on (and two while residents were occupied with other cases down the hall).

I rotated with a team of twelve peers that included a friend named 'Preacher Sam.' He wasn't really a preacher, but he was so dedicated to his church that his evangelical efforts often made their way onto the ward. When the residents and attending physicians wrote our grade summaries, Preacher Sam was chastised for his 'sense of humor, sometimes inappropriate and in need of self-monitoring as it distracts from the talents of this brilliant student.' While mine read 'clinically sound student and eager to learn, but needs to keep personal religious feelings out of the clinic setting.' Preacher Sam, was crushed, as they had the two of us confused the whole time! I was delighted - not only did he get blamed for my irreverent humor, his exam score was six points higher than mine!

The third year experience is usually as follows: in OB/Gyn and Internal Medicine you are overwhelmed by the scope of the information and the workload. During the Pediatric rotation you catch all the bugs the kids bring in and stay sick. During the Surgery months you hold retractors for hours and get yelled at by surgeons, and during Psychiatry you realize that you will be a psychiatrist, or that you could *never* be a psychiatrist, but you will always remember your psych patients. (For most students, it is their first encounter with individuals who are truly psychotic. If you want instant dialogue, ask any doctor you call on if he or she recalls their psych patients from third year.)

The final year involves some standard rotations (such as outpatient medicine) and several electives. I chose one particular research rotation in psychiatry, where I met an attending whose mission is much like yours - he believes it is best to do research that could help thousands of patients he'll never meet, rather than see them one at a time.

You also begin interviewing for residency spots during this last year, and then take part II of the National Medical Boards. This part focuses on the clinical rotations you have just experienced, and is regarded as a bit easier than Part I, but no walk in the park. My strongest score was in psychiatry, and my weakest was obstetrics. After the long day, George and I headed to our apartments together and tried to recall as many questions and answers as we could. I recall naming various obstetrical cases and getting his input on my decisions – he kept saying things like 'with that answer, you killed the baby.' And 'with that one, you killed mom, and baby is in the ICU.' And at one point, 'wow, with that answer, you managed to kill the dad who was in the room videotaping the event...' fortunately for pregnant couples all over the Southeastern US, I chose psychiatry.

Residency

Choosing a residency involves the 'Match' system. Students send applications to schools of their choice, and if they are impressed with what they see, an interview is scheduled. Students then rank the schools in order of preference, and the schools rank the students they met. For each student, and each program, the two highest numbers are matched-up as closely as possible. It works perfectly when you rank a school number one and they feel as strongly about having you. When there is not such a perfect match, a computer program sorts it out.

It's important for the current residents to interview applicants as well as the faculty, because they will obviously be working with these new doctors every day. During my third year, a doctor interviewed to switch to our program. At the time he was already in a program across the country, in fact, on the West coast. He said it was just time for a change of scenery. His references were fine, his grades excellent so far, so why move across the country for just one more year? We eventually rejected his application when we learned he had some personal issues to sort out. He had managed to get himself engaged to five separate women out west! Time for a change of scenery indeed…

Residencies vary in length – some are three years (such as pediatrics, internal medicine, obstetrics/gynecology) while others are longer (five years of surgical training). Some openings are very competitive (such as ophthalmology, radiology, or dermatology) while some specialties suffer from a shortage of applicants.

After the first year of residency (often called 'Internship,' whether or not you are an 'Internist' studying Internal Medicine - confused yet?) you take Part III of the National Medical Boards. After passing this, you advance from the 'training' medical license given to interns to a full medical license; theoretically, you could begin your own practice at this point. But, of course, this is unwise, and virtually all of us finish our residencies and take a specialized board exam. We do, however, commonly 'moonlight,' or work in clinics or ER's while residents for extra income.

The board exam process is the gold standard of certification. For example, to call yourself a psychiatrist, you must be board certified by the American Board of Psychiatry and Neurology. The disciplines are actually very much linked, and we share some aspects of training. In fact, our god, I mean, our profession's originator, Sigmund Freud, was a neurologist by training. Roughly one third of our written boards are neurology questions. After passing this exam, you are invited to take oral boards, in which you interview a patient in front of three examiners, and then enjoy an extensive grilling by them. They are instructed to give no feedback on your answers, not letting on if you are right or wrong, but the suspense ends when an evaluation letter arrives several weeks later.

A specialist has completed a residency in a general discipline, or some core requirements of that discipline, and further studied as a 'Fellow' in a more specific area - such as the surgeon who continues study in neurosurgery, or internist who attends a fellowship in oncology to treat cancer patients. Fellowships vary greatly in length, but the following is a table of basic residency durations:

Residency Lengths

- Family medicine – 3 years
- Internal medicine – 3 years
- General surgery – 5 years
- Obstetrics and Gynecology – 4 years
- Psychiatry – 4 years
- Pediatrics – 3 years

The Medical Model

The overall 'medical model' is a hierarchical system: at the top of the pyramid is the attending physician, ultimately in charge of the care, below are the residents, doing the actual day to day evaluations and treatment and then reporting to the attending. The students are there to absorb as much as they can and help the residents with various tasks involved in patient care (the slang term for this is 'scut-monkey'). The residents and the students are frequently put on the spot in morning rounds, and expected to think on their feet. The system can be abusive in the wrong hands, but the overall emphasis is on the ultimate responsibility we have as physicians. Soon, we are launched in the world, and we have to know those answers without a team of other doctors and students to help out. I recall being in my first week of private hospital practice and seeing an entire treatment team look at me after discussing a difficult case, and wait for the answer to 'what are we going to do?' What was new was that I had no one to turn to for an answer, and nobody was leaving until I gave one. The good news was, if I made one up, they didn't seem to know the difference.

I write about all this leaving out perhaps the most critical component: nursing. As attendings and residents we can write all the orders in the chart that we want, but none of it happens without our nurses. Don't neglect this overworked, underpaid, and often unappreciated group of professionals. They are our front-line caregivers who can benefit from your support and educational skills as well.

Reps along the way

After a long call night during my obstetrics rotation; tired, hungry and broke, I left a call room because I heard there was free food down the hall. I met my first rep that morning, who was the first person in twenty-four hours to treat me with respect, feed me, and even took the time to educate me about a new antibiotic. What did he ask in return? Only for a small bit of time. To this day, I remember his drug, his message, and his kindness.

Throughout the rest of my clinical rotations I enjoyed these interactions, and as a resident I found your services invaluable during the rapid (and continuing) expansion of psychiatric medications. If you encounter departments where reps are not welcome, seek out opportunities to educate the residents at dinner programs or other venues off campuses. Our residents should not miss out on your educational services, even if their administrators are short-sighted.

Some of the prescription habits I developed as a resident stay with me today, particularly when I am treating illnesses outside my area of specialty. Pay particular attention to your resident, student, and nurse customers - your efforts could pay off for years!

Summary:

- Doctors are trained in a hierarchical system.

- The 'medical model' traditionally involves one clinician at the top of the pyramid ultimately responsible for the decisions.

- Medical schools and residency programs have made great strides in rounding out the educational experience in recent years, but the volume and complexity of information has kept the overall experience fairly traditional.

- Students and residents are often your most appreciative and eager customers, and your impact on their prescription habits could last for years.

- Nurses are our front-line caregivers, and educating them is essential as well.

'I'm sure you're wondering, Dr. Perry, 'what advantages do Bat-pills have for my patients?'

Chapter 2

The Basics of Medical Decision Making

On hospital rounds today, I saw twenty patients and wrote an average of three separate medication orders per patient (some medications were added, some discontinued, and some were adjusted). Why did I pick the ones I did? Why quetiapine for patient X with psychosis and risperidone for patient Y? You need to know. The basics of medical decision-making are at the heart of your job: if you hope to influence prescription habits you need to know why we are making the medication choices we are. Today, there were sixty separate opportunities for a medication decision, and that did not include the two nurse practitioners that I supervise, nor the people who called (patients and other clinicians) for medication advice. And that was all before lunchtime...

The Differential Diagnosis

Medical decisions start with an accurate diagnosis. The process of evaluating the patient's symptoms, and then considering all the most likely causes is referred to as creating a 'differential diagnosis.'

Physicians are trained not to miss anything. As mentioned in chapter 1, a patient with an anxiety disorder may complain of a headache, yet so will a patient with a brain tumor. Chest pain can result from pneumonia, muscle spasms, a heart attack, or about seventy other conditions. When faced with a complaint, we are trained to consider everything, and narrow it down to a list of possible causes. Then we test, question, examine, scan, do whatever is necessary to find the exact diagnosis among these likely candidates.

An example of this process from today's hospital rounds involves a patient we'll call Mark. He is twenty-six and was hospitalized due to hallucinations. They were quite unusual and involved seeing other people, including his wife, transforming into monsters with hideous faces. I met her as he was admitted and found her to be quite lovely, but also quite unwilling to provide me with any information about Mark. He had been hospitalized once before, in his words, for 'stress,' so we faxed a release for records to that previous facility. His initial diagnosis was "Psychosis, N.O.S." which means, he has psychotic symptoms, but we're not sure why (Not Otherwise Specified). Sometimes patients with Bipolar Illness hallucinate, schizophrenics certainly do, and of course drugs can cause psychotic symptoms. He could also have a seizure disorder or even a brain tumor. So, the differential in this 26 year-old with psychosis includes Schizophrenia, Bipolar Disorder, a drug-induced problem, a brain lesion, or a seizure disorder.

Soon, his records arrived, his physical was complete, his laboratory studies were back, and I was able to chat with his wife on the phone without Mark present. Then I had a diagnosis. His neurological exam was fine, showing no evidence for a tumor or other lesion. His records showed a history of admissions, but not simply for 'stress,' but specifically for the stress caused by using $500 worth of cocaine each day. His wife said he was abusing sleeping pills and narcotics. When he took too many, he hallucinated. He didn't need an antipsychotic, as he led me to believe, he needed detoxification. Mark's exam was also changing by now, his pulse was elevated, his stomach cramping, and he was sweaty, anxious, and uncomfortable. The picture was now very clear.

What is important in this example is not the diagnosis, but the process of making the correct one – we consider everything, then explore, examine, and test – all to narrow it down to the most likely one diagnosis. Also, by the time I stared a detox regimen, his drug

12

screen was positive for barbiturates, cocaine, marijuana and opiates – a clean sweep! (You may wonder why Mark didn't just tell me the truth in the first place – but this is one of the challenging aspects of clinical care, sometimes a patient will not share everything, either consciously or subconsciously.)

Risk – Benefit Ratios

Everything we do in medicine conveys some risk, however small, and every medication or procedure is intended to have benefit. If the benefit outweighs the risk, we usually proceed. If risk is greater than potential benefit, we look for other options. Here are a couple of scenarios that highlight this very thought process:

Jane was a twenty-two year old involuntarily hospitalized to my service. She had a drug screen positive for cocaine and methadone. She was also hearing voices that told her to kill herself and specifically to 'cut her wrists.' She said it was Satan talking to her and at times he would direct her to assault other patients. Monday was looking pretty cheerful on the ward, but the case was not particularly unusual for our service, until we discovered that her pregnancy test was positive!

Helen is a thirty-one year old who was seeking help for depression and also some advice regarding whether to proceed with chemotherapy. She had breast cancer. After the initial surgical procedure, her doctor recommended chemo. Helen was also pregnant. And, one more detail, she is a lawyer.

In Jane's case, she is clearly psychotic and risks harming herself, other patients, and her child if she is untreated. The antipsychotic medication I recommended was a category "C" drug (see the Glossary), and clearly the benefit outweighed the risk. Further, she was about three months along, so the baby's organ systems had formed. If any harm had been done, it was from the illicit drugs, and worrying about the risks of a badly needed antipsychotic was pointless. Benefit outweighed risk – Jane did get better with the medication and was monitored in a supervised situation until delivery (and yes, the little guy survived the illegal (and legal) drugs just fine and is perfectly healthy).

Helen was told that her survival rate would increase with chemo, but from 88% only to 92%. The risk to her baby, however, was significant. In fact, there was even a risk of spontaneous abortion. The baby was healthy on ultrasound studies, heart rate was good, all organs systems looked fine, and so Helen asked why she should risk her child's life for an extra 4% chance on her survival? For Helen, risk was far greater than the 4% of potential benefit.

Further, clinicians usually consider the least risky alternative as the first option in therapy, while more risky alternatives are considered if there is no response, or a less than optimal response to the safest choice. This is one reason why your safety profiles are so critical to your missions. Never simply gloss over safety data, pregnancy ratings, side effect profile, and common adverse events. These issues are critical in choosing the right option for any patient.

A Self-Correcting Process

In many ways, medical decision-making is safe guarded and even self-correcting. After evaluating the patient in an all-inclusive fashion and then using that information to decide the most likely diagnosis, the next step is testing the hypothesis. This can involve diagnostic tests (EEG's, MRI's, so on) or can involve a prescription.

A recent example involves a 54 year-old lady on my ward who was hospitalized after bringing her dogs to work. No, it wasn't pet day, she was just scared they wouldn't be safe if left alone, and worried for her safety too. She had been anxious and paranoid for weeks, not sleeping and very depressed. Her exam also showed some memory impairment. Her physical exam was normal, as were all laboratory studies. Her diagnosis was Major Depression with psychosis, and she improved somewhat in the hospital with antidepressant and antipsychotic meds. But after being home a month, she was again paranoid, confused, and unable to work. She had failed to fully respond to the standard measures of antidepressant and antipsychotic medication. A new workup included an MRI of the brain, more extensive laboratory work and screens for autoimmune disorders. Again, these tests were normal, but a more detailed battery of psychological testing showed her memory was much more impaired than one would expect simply from depression. Despite her young age, we diagnosed her with dementia, most likely Alzheimer's type. She was also depressed, but her drug regimen now included Namenda (for dementia) as well as the antidepressant and antipsychotic.

Thus, the process of all inclusive thinking and repeatedly testing the most likely hypotheses will usually create a path to the right answer.

What do we do when no correct answers emerge and we are stumped? We consult our specialists!

Summary

- When a patient is evaluated, a list of potential diagnoses are considered, this is called the 'differential diagnosis.'

- The most likely diagnoses are tested for, and eventually treated.

- All interventions (prescriptions, procedures, surgeries) carry some risk and all are intended to have benefit.

- If benefit outweighs risk, we proceed, but if risk is considered too great, we choose another therapy.

- Ideally, a therapy conveys tremendous benefit and zero risk.

- The exact risk/benefit ratio will vary widely from treatment to treatment, but as a rule, physicians are likely to choose a low risk option as their starting point (i.e., risk concerns usually trump benefit).

- Because your customers are trained to consider all possible causes of a symptom, and because we test our hypothesis, the process is, in this regard, self-correcting.

- We can always rely on consultants and experts in specialized areas for back-up, again, making sure no diagnosis goes unrecognized.

The doctor will see your insurance forms now...

Chapter 3

The Psychology Behind Prescription Choices

I admitted a young lady to the hospital today because she was not responding to her antidepressant. She had missed two weeks of work, was crying much of the day, and was even reporting suicidal thoughts. Her psychiatrist had chosen a commonly used medication a week ago believing it would be best for her anxiety. I discussed another option with her, and changed her medication to the one I believed would work more quickly. We had chosen two agents from a list of over twenty that could have been effective – he had picked one based on the patient's clinical profile, while I had decided one was superior to the rest, regardless of her particular type of depression. This illustrates two common methods for choosing a medication when all are deemed efficacious. (The best part of this example is that we live in a time when either option gets the patient better.)

For the sake of discussion, we are talking about any group of medications in which efficacy is considered equal, and your job involves explaining why we should pick yours over the others in the class.

The Overriding Principle:

This principle guided my choice in the example above (and frequently does in other cases). If I believe one agent alleviates depressive symptoms faster than the others, then it only makes sense that I decide it is the best place to start, or the best one to switch a patient to when they are not responding to current therapy. This is particularly important to me since I am a hospital-based physician, and many of my depressed patients are hospitalized due to suicidality. But this pattern can be seen in any specialty. I know a physician who prescribes the same antihypertensive to over seventy percent of his patients in need of one because he believes "it protects the kidneys best of all." You get the idea, sometimes a clinical aspect of that therapy is so important it becomes an overriding principle.

Your task is to find out what is most important in a medication class for each customer and explore with them the ways your agent may fit their overriding principle. You have just learned that I see inpatients, many of whom are hospitalized specifically because they want to take their lives, so rapid onset is a major concern. Now, I have been challenged politely (and less politely) at meetings and in print by my colleagues who disagree with my overriding principle, and perhaps data will emerge in the future that will allow me to stand up at a national psychiatry meeting and say 'I stand corrected.' But the key point for the rep is that it really does not matter to the example whether or not the principle is true for every patient. My colleagues and I can debate and write opinions about the speed of onset of different antidepressants all day, your job is to see where your agent has a role for my patients.

Whatever your approach, don't simply join the colleagues that disagree with my overriding principle – explore it, ask about where the belief comes from, and use this as an opportunity to increase dialogue, don't create an argument. Back to my specific example: there are reps for competitor drugs who try to argue with me about my convictions, and there are those who are eager to look at articles on the topic and learn more about the issue. The latter are focused on how their agent may help the patients. You can guess which ones get plenty of my time.

The Patient Profile

The patient I mentioned above was very nervous, tremulous, and couldn't eat or sleep – the lay term is probably "a nervous wreck." My colleague focused on the anxiety symptoms associated with her depression and those symptoms drove his thinking. He felt one agent was better than the rest at reducing anxiety. I disagree, but again, for the purpose of the discussion, it doesn't matter which of us is right! (In fact, for this patient, the agent he chose increased her anxiety level despite his theory) Your task involves seeing where your drug fits a profile and how it may help those very patients.

In many classes where efficacy is considered equal, a great deal of marketing has focused on patient profiles that best fit a medication's benefits, some even highlight side effects as potential benefits for certain profiles. Profiles *do* resonate with doctors, and patients often list a symptom cluster that exactly fits your detail message. But, the down side of this type of selling is that it may narrow the field of candidates too much. Why deprive patients of an agent they may benefit from just because their profile differs from the typical case?

Positive and Negative Tags

As a rep who is detailing drug X, you have a great knowledge of the product and can quickly name several positive attributes, such as drug X has a low potential for interacting with other drugs, or drug X is the only one of its class with an FDA indication for Dengue fever. These are called positive tags, and they stick in the customer's mind. Ask any doctor which antidepressant has no risk of sexual side effects, or which NSAID is safest for the renal system in long-term use, or which antihypertensive will not negatively affect a normal blood pressure - these three medications will be instantly recalled by most informed clinicians. The positive tags are powerful tools that can help get your product to the patients that will benefit. Like patient profiles, they can get our attention long after you have left and even while we are interviewing patients. But, beware of the negative tags…

As you have been responsibly promoting your product and planting positive tags, the competition has been out there planting negative ones, such as, 'drug X can cause QTc interval change and puts patients at risk for arrhythmias,' or 'drug X causes excessive weight gain, or even cataracts!' Negative tags are also powerful, and sadly, they can be highly effective even if they are not true! (We will deal with blatant lies about your products in Chapter 8.)

Specific to choosing a prescription, remember that a negative tags is a reason *not* to consider a product, and a way the doctor can simplify the choices and more quickly make a decision. Why discuss five drug options with a patient and pick the right one together, when it is so much easier to narrow the list and, for example, decide 'drug A causes weight gain, drug B is the worst for drug interactions, drug C has cardiac risks, and drug D is too expensive.' All we have left is drug X! That was quick and easy!

Negative tags, and lies about your product, are like frivolous law suites, you know they're ridiculous and a waste of time and energy, but you still have to defeat them. How? Using logic, persuasion, and whatever resources you need - literature to back you up, expert opinion, and never forget the most important method of defeating the negative tag: encourage the doctor to trust his or her own experience!

If we discuss this experience in the context of the negative tags with you, then we will instantly fall back on this knowledge when a competitor attempts to negatively characterize your drug. A rep once told me that one of my most utilized antipsychotics 'had no proven efficacy;' and I instantly said, 'there are ten hospitalized patients getting better on that drug right now! If the drug is no good, then I have more skill than I thought!'

Spreaders and Non-spreaders

It is no surprise that primary care providers and specialists have different prescription patterns. In general, the majority of primary care clinicians tend to prescribe two or three medications from a specific class, and if none are successful, they refer to specialists for other options. Some, about 30%, will spread their prescriptions throughout a class, showing no particular preference for one drug. For specialists, the opposite is true, 70% spread the choices around, while a minority will pick two or three favorites.

If your product is already a top choice, then keep up the great work! When things are going well, you should keep marketing as if they weren't. Speaking from the unusual perspective of the specialist who has a few favorite choices in each class, I can tell you that my loyalty to each number one choice is highly dependent on the educational value provided by the reps for those products. If your agent is not a top choice for a customer and you believe it should be, don't try to replace the top drug through attacks, simply try to persuade us that your drug deserves to be there too.

As I said, I am not the typical specialist because I tend to stick to a few top choices. As a clinician who now only sees hospitalized patients, I often use the overriding principle of 'speed of response' to guide my decisions. Also, the hospital setting allows me the advantages of combining medications or rapidly escalating doses, which are strategies too aggressive for typical outpatient settings. When reps try to displace a top choice, I can sense myself discounting their details, because I see my patients benefiting from the strategies that focus on those medications. Don't bash the top choices, align yourself with them, and compare your product favorably with them.

Office-Trials of New Drugs

When a new agent arrives on the scene, it is most often greeted with excitement. For example, in a few weeks, we expect a new agent for Alzheimer's dementia. Patient family members have already called to inquire if their loved-one is a candidate, or ask 'can I have samples?' and 'how soon?' I only know what I have read in journals and on Medline, and have no hands-on experience with the drug yet. However, I am calling five families as soon as it is available, and will give them a prescription or samples.

Monitor these office trails closely. You need to be available for instruction and support, particularly because the patients who get these meds first are usually the most severe and treatment resistant cases. I will be keeping a closer watch than usual on the new agent's effect, and this initial experience will likely influence future use.

The Curse of Too Many Exclusion Criteria

A colleague is currently conducting a study on a new treatment for depression. It involves the use of magnets to create an electrical field, which is then used to stimulate areas of the brain. I was excited to hear of his new procedure and had five patents in mind that I thought would benefit. I called to discuss them, but learned that they did not meet the study's criteria, and he emailed the exact exclusion criteria to me. He was hopeful I would help supply the study with needed patients. But despite the high volume of patients we see in our hospitals and clinics, I have referred none (not even the five I initially had in mind). His criteria for excluding subjects were too vast! There were so many to consider (to participate in the study, the patients could be on no medications, could have no past antidepressant failures, could have no personality disorders, no history of substance abuse, no medical illness, no brain lesions – so on, to which I emailed back, asking why these people might be depressed at all!).

My mindset has completely changed - I initially sought out patients who might benefit, but now, I go through my day never thinking of the study. I have mentally 'given up' on the whole idea!

Why is this story important to your mission? Because there are drugs that we 'mentally give up on' as well. When a new injectable agent became available for our patients, I was an enthusiastic supporter. I insisted our pharmacy stock the drug, despite formulary limits and protests from the pharmacy director about cost. I used it several times during its first week of availability. That was only one month ago. Now I have mentally given up – I don't consider it an option anymore.

Why such a rapid transition?

The cumulative effect of too many negatives, too many reasons to exclude the drug from the list of options: cost (at least $200 per injection), pain associated with administration, which we correlated with a low follow-up rate of return appointments (where another painful injection was expected), and a cumbersome storage and usage procedure. Further, none of my colleagues in the community were on board yet, so my referrals to them for continuation of these injections when the patent was discharged from the hospital were simply not being accommodated. Any one of these is a significant barrier to overcome, but the cumulative effect was overwhelming.

But, I still believe it is a good option for some patients, and I want them to benefit. I took the initiative and emailed my rep. 'Help!' was how I began. I told her we needed to figure out a way to get this product to the patients who will benefit and I explained all the obstacles.

Will your customers take this kind of initiative, even after they have given up on a product? They will if you convince them that your product is an excellent option for most patients, and maybe the best option for some. If they believe in the benefits of the product and the results it will give, then neglecting it is not a choice. That belief is what you can convey, and that is the only approach to overcoming the cumulative weight of too many negatives.

Letting the Product Speak for Itself!

As clinicians, we trust our patients to report what is working and what is not. A partner summed it up this way 'my patients tell me how to be a doctor, if I listen to them, I learn what works and what doesn't.'

This powerful lesson will serve you well, if your product is working and patients are improving, let your doctors tell you. Positive experiences should be emphasized, negative ones explored. If you believe in the product, convey your confidence and encourage use. If efficacy, and tolerability are there, and you get the message out - prescriptions will follow.

Summary:

- Prescription habits differ from primary to specialty care – most specialists use the full range in a class, while most primary care clinicians focus on a few favorite agents.

- Some doctors prescribe an agent based on an important principle that overrides most any other concern, usually it is safety related.

- Medications are also commonly prescribed based on the clinical profile of the patient, who is therefore best served by a particular agent targeting that profile.

- Positive tags are attributes that allow a customer to instantly recall your product and promote use.

- Negative tags decrease use and are usually planted by the competition.

- Tags are usually effective, even when they are not true.

- New agents are often greeted with enthusiasm and informal 'office trials' are monitored, and can vastly impact future use.

- Too many exclusion criteria can overwhelm a product and it may never be considered for use - unless you persuade us the barriers can be overcome, and it is worth it to the patient to make the effort.

- A good drug will speak for itself, provide the stage, and allow it to do the talking.

THE REP GUIDE TO —
DOCTOR-SPEAK:

Doctors:	~	English:
I need to get more experience with your drug...		Never use it...
I've had a setback or two...		Patient exploded on your drug...
Great to see you! Come on in! We've got to talk!!!		I need a grant...
It's going just fine...		what is your drug again??
Have you changed Companies?		Who the heck are you???

A.Cavali 04

Chapter 4

The Three Main Influences on Prescription Habits

We have explored the psychology of choosing one drug over another when all are equally effective, but what makes a particular choice grow into a habit?

The influences that lead a clinician to repeatedly prescribe one medication over the others have been explored in focus groups and survey studies, and also by tracking prescription patterns after an influential detail or contact with an expert. When asked which is most important in determining prescription habits given the choices of clinical research, expert opinion, or recommended practice guidelines, physicians will choose:

None of the above.

All of the above are important, and do contribute to clinical opinions and practice habits. For example, I am well versed on the American Psychiatric Association's published guidelines on treating Major Depression, Bipolar Illness, and Delirium - illnesses that I treat every day. And every day, certain cases arise in which I disagree with some aspects of these guidelines. Medicine is too unique an endeavor, and too patient-specific to make any set of guidelines work for every patient.

Experts are wonderful resources, in fact, I am one! I enjoy getting calls and emails from physicians who may have read one of my articles and ask various questions, and I routinely contact other experts when I need advice. And sure, clinical research is the framework from which we build a sound practice, but study patients are not characteristic of most of your customers' patients (for example, a rep recently asked me if I saw patients responding according to the timetable in the clinical trials of her antipsychotic – I said, 'No, I escalated the dose much faster, and see results more rapidly.' (And I also made it clear that my last patient to benefit from her agent was not only psychotic, but had a recent head injury, a positive drug screen for several compounds, and a hyperthyroid condition – any one of which would exclude him from a study.)

None of these important sources is the final word in making a medication a repeated choice, and eventually becoming a prescription habit.

Prescription habits are most influenced by:

1. **Personal Experience**
2. **Personal Experience**
3. **and ... the personal experiences of trusted colleagues**

Here's an example: a new medication has arrived for treating schizophrenia. I had used it in about fifteen patients over the past month but none had done particularly well – most became more agitated over a few days, and the rest experienced no improvement. This month's issue of a respected psychiatric journal listed two case reports titled 'Increased Agitation on Drug X,' which confirmed my impressions. Though I've just discussed a very small sample size and it amounts to purely anecdotal evidence, including the published cases, still, what are the chances that I will start using this drug as my first line agent? Also consider that in a managed care environment, acutely psychotic patients are often allowed only three or four days to stabilize!

Because of our lack of success, I invited the representative for drug X to do an in-service for our staff. It was very helpful – we learned that we were dosing the drug correctly and monitoring for the expected side effects, so we're on the right track as far as proper usage. But what should we make of our lack of success? I still didn't hear enough to try the drug again. I am simply not confident that patients will improve.

...and I said, 'Of course your spouse can come to the program...' how about you?

After the in-service, I called a friend who is the Medical Director of a large number of mental health clinics in our region. He is well respected in the psychiatric community and has put far more patients on this medication than I have. Though my experience has been less than optimal, I always trust what this friend says.

What I have just alluded to is the issue of confidence: in effect, how sure am I this medication will work? Good experiences build confidence, and poor ones erode it. If an agent fails once or twice in our first few patients, we are usually not concerned (and may even expect a few initial failures in treatment-resistant cases), however, repeated problems begin to solidify a negative opinion. But, more importantly, patients will lose confidence. Take for example, antidepressants – of all the people who need medication for depression, only about half ever come to a physician's attention. Of that group only 40% will actually take the recommended antidepressant for over a six-month period! You can see how important it is for these patients to feel confident about their therapy, to know it is working, experience few if any side effects, and stay on their meds.

A Few Tips on *Interpreting* Personal Experience

Interpretation? Medical experience is objective, right? Well, as with much of medicine, the answer is 'yes and no.' Here are the main ways personal experience becomes personal *impression*, which may or may not be accurate:

1. **Generalizing Limited Data:** as with my example above, a small sample size will get generalized into an impression. When colleagues have asked what I think of drug X, I say 'patients tend to get worse on it.' I know this contradicts all

the clinical studies, but I still generalized my limited experience (and I am a clinician who not only participates in research, but is an expert on medical decision making!)

2. **Limited Use Perceived as Extensive:** have you ever had a doc tell you they use your drug 'all the time,' and the prescription data reflects far less usage? Sure, some may be misleading you, but the majority probably perceive their use as more extensive *precisely because it is less*! The limited use, because it is so rare, is paradoxically more memorable. Again, back to my example, drug X, which I used a great deal and then stopped. If I use it once a week now, I remember that patient and their response, while the drug I use twenty times a week I tend to lose track of.

3. **Miracle Pills:** when I was a resident, I recall one case so challenging that no other resident would take it over when I left! The patient would weekly attempt suicide, sometimes having the resident on call paged just to say she was overdosing while on the phone with them! So severe was her Borderline Personality, that a week of stability was a reasonable goal (the other residents all decided to pay her one-way bus fare to whatever town I moved to...which I kept secret for some time). Now, when she achieved stability with a new drug for controlling mood swings, and remained out of the hospital for months, that miracle cure became my first choice for every Borderline. Great experiences (maybe even a single one) are often generalized just like the negative experiences.

Opinions of Trusted Colleagues

So, what about my friend's opinion of drug X? The famous Dr. Perry had an interesting story: yes, he too had limited success, out of about fifty new patients, most had not done well and some had indeed become more agitated on the drug. But there were two very dramatic responses. Family members called it a miracle cure for those two patients. One story involved a very treatment resistant schizophrenic who had tried every other medication available at one time or another, and various combination therapies (two or more antipsychotics, or an antipsychotic and a mood stabilizer). He was so paranoid that he rarely opened his door or answered the phone, and family members would leave groceries outside his apartment once a week. When he did manage to come in for appointments, his skin was in bad shape, as he apparently had tactile hallucinations and would scratch himself quite extensively. However, after three weeks on drug X he was coming for appointments, his skin was clearing, and he even smiled and asked Dr. P how *he* was doing. Drug X had been a success. "Who knows," my friend said, "maybe this was the first one he really took consistently, and maybe it was just right for his system."

So, Dr. Perry had found it to be a miracle pill for two, but cautioned that about a third had gotten more agitated, as in my experience (if you are aware of how antipsychotics work, you know it is not uncommon for a patient to get worse for a few days before showing improvement, and we discussed why this phenomenon may be more commonly associated with drug X).

Thus, my opinion is still that drug X is probably not the best option most of the time, but for that occasional treatment-resistant case, it may just be the answer. I am willing to keep trying it, but not often. This is not exactly the answer our rep for Drug X wants to hear. But believe me, she is a lucky rep! As her customer, I am choosing to tell her exactly what my experiences have been, what my colleague said, and where I stand now. To serve our patients in the best manner possible, I need to make sure my understanding and use of drug X is completely on target, and the dialogue must continue – so, what should the representative do with this information?

1. Encourage more experience in cases I find appropriate.
2. Explore whether these first attempts were in treatment-resistant patients.
3. Tell me if the positive experiences Dr. Perry had were similar to what she was hearing from others.
4. Keep looking for an expert I respect who may have a different view to share.

She actually did arrange a lunch with a speaker in town promoting her product. We had a great dialogue, and I learned he had no doubts about efficacy, but again the situation remains unresolved in my mind because we see very different populations.

There were other products and situations I could have written about, such as the colleague who reported the opposite of my experience and convinced me to try that agent a few more times, but that would be much less instructive. I could have also listed examples where experts concur and thus solidify each other's opinions. But, this example is more realistic, and the rep is left in a more ambiguous situation. The rep that can work through the difficult challenge of the more diffuse clinical situation will excel.

Summary:

- Personal experience drives prescription habits.

- Clinical trials, expert opinion, and published guidelines are all extremely valuable, but all are trumped by the impact of patients in front of the physician, doing well or poorly on an agent.

- Small sample sizes and anecdotal experience, whatever their limitations, are in the forefront of your customer's mind when prescribing.

- Your job involves finding out as much as you can about those experiences and making them the focus of your detail.

- Good personal experiences (such as 'miracle cures') and bad ones (allergic reactions) are also generalized and remembered predominantly.

- Few aspects of medicine are crystal clear, and attitudes may be forming or ambiguous when you meet the customer. This is a barrier to be met head on with creativity, perseverance, and passion.

Perhaps you should double the Prozac…'

Part II

The Art of Medical Selling

Reps who focus on what is best for patients are also focused on what is best for their doctors and their companies. It's a win-win-win when patients come first...

Leah Payne R.N.

Chapter 5

Rep Basics

Thanks to your excellent work, you have set the bar extremely high for yourselves. The medical community expects the following from you:

- A professional dress and demeanor. As residents, we were instructed by our chairman to dress well, but not so fashionably that we ourselves become a distraction to the patient. This is good advice for you also. Your self-presentation should enhance your message, not distract from it.

- Universal courtesy to all staff and patients you encounter. Once again, advice from our chairman, Dr. McCall, will serve you well. He treated everyone with the same degree of respect, from visiting faculty, students, to the man who came by once a week to water the plants. You will encounter numerous strangers throughout your day, and you have probably noticed that having a company tag on your lapel means strangers will approach you and ask for information. You will frequently be asked by patients in waiting rooms (and sometimes in parking lots) for advice on your drug. Remember the phrase 'your doctor is the best one to ask about that!'

- A rapid turn around on information and services requested. Again, you are victims of your success, as the requested study, or those excellent reports from your medical affairs department are usually expected soon after the request.

Sadly, such outstanding service is often unacknowledged, but if the requested information is late or never arrives... you know the rest of that story.

- Easy and reliable access to your services. Don't hesitate to give out your mobile numbers to key docs. Remember the rule of accessibility! We expect your services frequently but rarely tell you how often.

But most importantly, we expect credibility.

Credibility is all you really have to sell. I often correct the misperception that you are salespeople. This label is a disservice that ignores the reality that you are the front line of physician education when it comes to pharmaceuticals. So what do you really *sell*? The fact that you are credible, that you can be trusted, that you can be relied upon for education.

Yes, the bar is set high and excellence is expected. But don't be intimidated by this, rise to the challenge! When you stand out among the excellent, you are the absolute best.

Summary:

- Your self-presentation should enhance your message, not distract from it.

- Show universal courtesy to all staff and patients you encounter.

- Be reliable and easy to access.

- Be credible and trustworthy.

- Rise to the challenge of excellence!

Chapter 6

Customer Expectations:
The Importance of Contact and Accessibility

"Why does my company care about the *number* of calls I make, shouldn't they worry about the *quality* of calls?"

This was the first question posed to me after my lecture 'Bringing Real Value to the Rep-Physician Relationship' at a company's training headquarters this fall (this question is also asked much more frequently in private settings without management around!). And isn't it just a matter of 'common sense'? Surely the management would rather have four excellent calls per day than ten calls in which the rep gets just a few seconds with the doctor and maybe a signature for samples, right?

Of course you would rather go through the day experiencing all physician visits as quality time, but each visit has its own value, however short or seemingly nonproductive:

Research indicates that your customers are expecting a certain frequency of contact with you – perhaps it is once a week, or maybe once a month, but we are expecting it. *Even if we never share this with you.* It sounds odd to have an expectation that we may never express, but when I surveyed physicians about how frequently they need and desire your input, the expectations were certainly there. They were, however, all over the map (responses ranged from three times a week to once every four months!). It is therefore impossible to generalize how often you should see all of your customers, or even every customer in a particular specialty. Initially, you'll have to rely on the guidance of your manager to space the frequency of calls in a new territory, but because the issue of frequency is extremely critical to your success, you'll have to discern, and then meet, each individual customer expectation.

Just how critical is meeting the customer's expectation of contact? When representatives are not visiting as frequently as expected, physicians listed these top four reasons:

1. I am not important to that representative.
2. That representative is not doing his/her job.
3. The products they represent are not first-line agents.
4. Their products can't compete with others in the class.

These responses (from a survey of 120 various physicians) are very enlightening. The first response was common among primary care and less common among specialties. These doctors simply assumed you didn't find them important – perhaps other clinicians had busier clinics, or other doctors are recognized as thought leaders and get most of your attention - who knows? What is important is that they drew a negative conclusion about themselves. I doubt any rep wants to be responsible for that idea in the customer's mind.

The second was more common in specialty care – perhaps the specialist is a bit more prone to consider himself important in your eyes, so if you don't show up as expected, you are lazy, not contributing to their practice or patient care. If you are not there, you are not doing your job.

The final two were *product* dependent, not specialty dependent – recall the most important factor in forming prescription habits? (The physician's **personal experience**) If we have a negative experience with your product, you need to be there to reinforce the basics, explore what may have gone wrong and address concerns. If something major is the problem, such as a patient having a severe adverse event, or even something minor, as the physician dosing the drug improperly and not seeing results, we will have a negative impression - and rep absence is often translated as meaning the product is the problem - not a first-line choice, not as good as the others.

Here's the challenging part: NONE of the physicians surveyed ever once discussed their expectations of contact with their representatives. Yet *all* had an opinion about how often they needed you, and further, every one of them expressed a negative conclusion when asked 'what if the representative never meets this unspoken expectation!'

Don't hesitate - ASK US! Obviously it is up to **you** to bring it up. I appreciate reps who ask me what I need from them and when we can next get together. This mindset will also help you transition from thinking and acting like a salesperson to living out the reality of who you really are - an educator, a partner in patient care, and a needed and reliable resource.

A rep at one of my seminars once asked 'how much contact is *too* much?' I responded for my whole profession by rephrasing the question as 'can we have too much medical education?' Of course not! The more you educate us, the better we are as clinicians, and the more patients benefit. The door is always open!

Summary:

- Each customer has an expectation of how often they need your input for patient care.

- Contact, however unproductive it may seem at times, is fulfilling a customer expectation. Meeting that expected frequency is critical.

- It is up to you to determine how often you need to call on a customer and meet that expectation.

- If you don't meet that frequency of detail visits, your customer will assume you are not doing your job, or that they are not important to you.

- If a customer has a negative experience with your product or finds it troublesome to use, or less efficacious, he/she will see rep absence as confirmation that the agent is not a first-line choice and should be avoided.

- Customers rarely share their specific expectations for contact spontaneously and need to be asked!

- No visit, however short, is wasted time. There is no such thing as too much contact!

'And you promise they will have no memory of the tissue sampling...'

Chapter 7

The Essential Elements of the Product Detail

The main emphasis of rep training is on the product detail. You spend most of your day pursuing those quality minutes in which you can explain the usage and the main advantages of your products. As physicians, we rely on that contact and education for our mission of service.

The product detail is at best a conversation. On the other extreme, it can sometimes be a rushed and one-sided dialogue. Keep striving towards a relaxed and conversational product detail, and if time is working against you, or customer pressures prevent full attention, ask if a few minutes later on in the day would work out better. Your message is too important to be rushed or skipped over.

Many reps ask if a conversational style means they should avoid an agenda, or a list of major points of emphasis. You can still be conversational and highlight the main clinical information you want us to remember. In fact, you should plan on covering these areas even if we don't ask about them! Much like a politician determined to get the message out, you can guide the conversation towards those key areas. Henry Kissinger was a master at this, and often started his news conferences by saying, 'Does anyone have any questions for my answers?'

Research shows over 97% of doctors want your input, and when you get access, the average amount of time spent detailing is an impressive 8 minutes. Of course, not all doctors are that receptive. I recall a colleague who famously passed a rep in his waiting room, patted his shoulder and said, 'consider yourself seen!' Fortunately, he had a better rapport with his patients. This same physician, and this same rep, recently had a very productive and enjoyable lunch together – for this doc, the office was not the setting for quality time.

When surveyed, physicians have different expectations for a new product detail than for details about familiar medications. Assuming you get the quality time, how should you use it?

For New Products:

How to Use it!

Your customers firstly want to know HOW TO USE THE PRODUCT. Teach us proper dosing, such as dose escalation schedules as done in studies, and how much is too much to give, whether absorption is affected by food - all the basics of safe and effective use. It may sound simple at times, but you need to cover it. Research also shows that an uncertainty about dosing will cause your docs to avoid the product altogether! Consider this example: a doc was considering a new antidepressant, one that was initially dosed twice a day and involved weekly escalation. A specialist instructed him that the recommended dose is too low for most patients and must be escalated more quickly, to a level 300mg higher than previously thought, and can be given once a day at bedtime. Faced with this contradictory information, this doc opted to avoid the product completely.

Because you don't want to seem insulting to the customer with information that is too basic, but you don't want to neglect this critical area, feel free to say '*I know you are already aware* that drug X is dosed twice a day...'

Indications:

Secondly, docs want to know what the product is indicated for. Pretty basic question, right? Well, many drugs have various uses, and it can seem overwhelming. Consider the SRI antidepressants: I have some depressed patients taking them, some are on them for obsessive-compulsive disorder, some have generalized anxiety disorder, others have panic attacks. Then there are a host of off label uses: chronic pain syndromes, migraine headaches, impulsivity, compulsive shopping, and even PMS. Further, some patients are children, but not all SRI's are FDA approved for children. Why, even my dog Caesar takes an SRI to reduce aggression! You can see how difficult it is for the non-specialist to keep up.

Though virtually all physicians feel comfortable prescribing an agent 'off label' when the clinical situation demands that it is the best option for the patient, the official indication is a framework of security to work from. Again, this may sound like simple data, but you must cover the FDA indication, again, uncertainty will usually lead us to use a product more familiar.

Trouble to Expect:

Docs also want to hear about side effects. We expect some with any agent, in fact, some of the worst side effects we see occur in our placebo wash-out phases of drug trials. Certainly cover the most common ones, and how best to handle them. The key thing to remember is that we may avoid the product not because it has potential side effects, but because we don't know what to do about them. If lowering dosage, splitting the dose, or adding an antidote helps, we need to know that.

The worst mistake to make when a customer reports a side effect and asks for your input is to convey that it is not possible, or not expected to occur, thereby discounting the report. Remember, it could always be a placebo effect, and it may be related to other medications, but you need to address all reports with appropriate weight. One particular medication was reported by our patients to cause weight gain at a much greater rate that we expected based on the clinical trials. The company stuck to the trial data and insisted for several months that this was not, in fact, occurring. When told that weight gain simply was not possible, one of my colleagues angrily said to the rep 'don't tell me I'm not seeing what I am seeing!'

The response should have been, 'let me investigate that, and talk to medical affairs.' Again, we simply need to know how to handle side effects. Valuable time is lost and customers lose confidence in your product and your credibility if side effects are denied.

Experience:

The experience of other clinicians is also important, not only that from clinical trials. When I speak for various antidepressants or antipsychotics, people always want to hear my experiences with the drug. They can read the studies for themselves - they come to hear my discussion of what to expect from the drug and to hear about the subtleties of its use.

Experience in other countries is also of interest, and many times we have a wealth of data from the European and other literature.

Cost:

Finally, your customers are concerned with cost. You will want to keep us informed as to which insurance plans cover the cost and to what extent. A current figure from a local drug store is very helpful, as we can then tell patients exactly what to expect.

Further, never describe you product as 'cheap' or 'cheapest.' Always say it is the best value or most competitively priced - more about cost in chapter 8.

Thus, the five elements your customers want covered in your new product detail are:

How to use it
Indications for use
Trouble to look for
Experience with the product, and
Cost.

The **H-I-T-E-C** model of detailing will never let you down! With this framework in mind, you can detail without visual pieces, and virtually anywhere, offices, break-rooms, parking lots...but try to avoid the parking lots – we'll appreciate that.

Familiar Product

What do your customers need to hear about products more familiar to them?

The top two answers were consistent across specialties:

1. Tell me something new! New data, new studies, interesting post marketing trials - this was the kind of information your customers requested. And:

2. Show some support for my use!

Huh??? Number two was not even relevant to the question! I asked what they needed to hear *clinically*! The question was specific to patient care, yet over seventy percent of the responders wanted their support, their belief in the product, to be recognized. In a way, this is relevant to patient care, as we support products that we believe are best for patients, and we certainly need your continuing input. This also reminds you to keep detailing when things are going well: we need more support and education with ever expanding usage.

Final word:

At a recent roundtable, a rep insisted on reading quotes from a study to the group. The problem was, we were having a fine discussion without them. Details that are too assertive will turn the customer off and distract from your message. Strive for the conversation, not the lecture!

Summary:

- Strive for the conversational detail, but keep your own agenda in mind.

- Remember the key points you want to cover and guide discussions towards them.

- The H-I-T-E-C model will serve as a framework of detailing for new products, and

- When detailing familiar products, share new data as soon as it is available.

- Always thank prescribers for their support and express your satisfaction that patients are benefiting.

'It says he's from managed-care, and here to further capitate your fees...'

Chapter 8

The Top Ten Obstacles to Getting Your Message Out

1. Time Pressure:

It's Monday morning, and I have just planned my day and week with three calendars – one for consulting services, one for medical director duties and hospital care, and one for personal events. You probably do the same thing with your calendar every Monday. As the director of a busy psychiatric practice (28 inpatient beds, consultation service, and outpatient offices) you can be sure several experts on medications for psychosis, depression, anxiety, and dementia are putting my name somewhere on their schedules. But the problem is, those calls are not planned on mine - most of you make traditional 'cold calls' hoping your customers have the time.

Here's a typical day – I start with inpatient rounds about 8 a.m., seeing the most severely ill first, then attend a treatment team meeting in which all disciplines (nursing, occupational therapy, case management) contribute ideas to patient care. Each patient is discussed individually and then we split up and I finish rounds. By lunchtime, about half of the twenty or so patients have been seen. I then see consultations - patients admitted to the hospital floors who are also in need of psychiatric management. These are patients who have overdosed, or perhaps those who experience mental status changes while hospitalized, or they may be in withdrawal from alcohol or drugs. These are some of the most common reasons I am called, but there are many others. My favorite recent one involved a man who had seizure-like episodes that were not from epilepsy, rather they were '*pseudo*-seizures.' Unfortunately he misunderstood the exact diagnosis, and asked that I help cure his '*voodoo*-seizures.' The neurologist assumed he was delusional, believing he had been cursed, but I think it was a simple misunderstanding.

Back at my ward, I suggested to a new patient that perhaps her imagination was getting the better of her and there was no need to barricade herself in her hospital bathroom – perhaps, I explained, she was just paranoid. She replied, "Well, if everyone here was trying to kill *you*, then you'd be paranoid too!!!" (…can't really argue with that.)

After hospital and consultation rounds, it's time to review the work of the clinicians I supervise, maybe have a session with a resident, or attend a hospital meeting. There are also numerous calls that come in through the day, the pager and cell phone to deal with, forms to be filled out, families of patients that need attention – you get the idea.

So:

How do you insert yourself into that kind of schedule and have a meaningful impact?

Answer:

Relationship

The relationship you develop with your customers will be the magic key of instant access. We stop what we are doing and make time for reps that we consider part of the treatment team, those that have a solid relationship with us, those who are our friends. With a solid relationship, you can transcend the whole game of trying to get access. Here's an example I used in the introduction to Lynda Goldman's book, *Prescription for Success*:

It was a busy day on the psychiatry service and the Messiah was waiting. At least a patient who thought he was 'The' Messiah. But his name was Herman, not particularly impressive for the chosen one, but he insisted on seeing me first – before any of the mere mortal patients. Before I started rounds, I learned that a rep was at the door to see me – someone well known to our staff. Jana, the rep, was seen first, and for a lengthy period of time. We kept the self-proclaimed Messiah waiting. Jana's visit was more important.

This may sound like a reversal of priorities, but Jana is part of our treatment team. I needed her information in order to prescribe medication for the patient I mentioned. He's a rather complex messiah, with several drug reactions in his history and a hesitancy about taking any medication. Spending time in dialogue with this particular rep *is* good patient care.

Jana has spent her time in the field wisely over the past two years. She has built a solid relationship with our staff and she is known as a credible resource, thus, she is a part of our treatment team not just another person wanting to take our time. She has transcended the whole game of access, as have her two partners, Nick and Mike.

I have seen the 'game' of access first hand, when I was recently the visiting lecturer in a large midwestern city. Three reps escorted me to a luncheon where I spoke to residents, students, attendings, and community physicians. The students were receptive and had numerous questions, and the residents on the whole were also interested. The attendings sat in the back, ate quickly, left early, and hid from the reps. They had hosted a luncheon with an expert on psychiatry and still were unable to get even a signature!

2. The Customer's Mind is Already Made Up

"Mr. Jones wants to be discharged today."

"Are the voices gone?" I asked his nurse.

"No, they still tell him he is the 'Angel of Death,' and then he mumbles something about getting a high-powered rifle."

After this frightening progress report I saw Mr. Jones, and there was nothing he could have said that would convince me to discharge him from the hospital. My mind was already made up before he spoke. He did plead his case for discharge: he would take all his medication, he would go to every follow-up appointment, he would follow any recommendation I had for him, but nothing he said mattered. Even if he had genuinely improved that morning after the nursing assessment, I still wouldn't have discharged him - the risk was too great.

What does this story have to do with you? Well, have you ever detailed a physician who had already decided not to use your product even before you had a chance to detail them? I actually saw a rep shortly after my rounds with Mr. Angel of Death. She wanted me to see that her drug was added to our hospital formulary. However, I had spoken to our pharmacy director weeks before and we concluded that since I was using the drug only three or four times per month it wasn't worth stocking. If a patient needed it, the pharmacy could obtain it in a few hours. I could sense her frustration- she covered the merits of the drug, including the cost savings it might bring, and when she realized she was getting nowhere with these arguments, finally added that it was important to her company to get the account with our hospital.

She and Mr. Jones both were faced with the difficult situation of dealing with someone whose mind is firmly made up. Unlike Mr. Jones, however, the rep was not psychotic and homicidal (although, I'm not so sure about her manger...). What she failed to realize was she actually *did* have a chance to persuade me despite the obstacle of my stubbornness. Where she went off course, however, is obvious. She became frustrated and began mentioning business issues that are unrelated to patient care. What should she have done?

Answer:

-   Ask Ask Ask! Explore why I only use the drug a few times a month. Seek to really understand what my hesitation is all about (she would have learned that I don't understand its mechanism, have difficulty crossing over with other agents, have uncertainty about correct dosing, and my partners have seen poor results thus far). You may be shrieking at the extent of these objections and of course they can't be easily answered, few are, but these are the starting points for discussion – not an ending point where opinions are left unchanged.

-   Arrange contact with an expert who does exactly what I do, but uses the product a great deal more. Let him or her explain why, and most importantly:

-   Keep the discussion patient focused! If we decide the drug is one of the best options for patients, it will obviously need to be stocked in the pharmacy. Good patient care is good business.

Even Better Answer:

Build a solid relationship with me and my staff so the dialogue is always open. There is still work to be done, but imagine how much easier the three tasks listed would be if I greeted her as a friend and dropped what I was doing to give her all the time she wanted?

3. Negative Misinformation

It has likely happened to each of you (or will) at some point in your career: you are visiting with a customer and hear an objection that begins with "the rep for Drug Z says..." and then a bizarre warning follows, such as "*your* drug causes spider-monkeys to go insane and kill humans..." This strikes you as particularly odd, not only because the allegation is false, but also because you are a responsible and credible representative who focuses on the advantages of your product, not the negative issues related to competitors. Further, as a credible resource to your customers, you would never think to make up misinformation!

What may be more amazing is the discovery that negative misinformation about your product has been circulated before your drug was even launched! Yes, before you detail customer number one on a new product, that customer may have already heard the tale of the spider monkey, or some other such tail, I mean, tale... And these lies unfortunately get traction - as Twain said, "a lie can travel halfway around the world while the truth is putting on its shoes..."

Maybe the homicidal monkeys were a bit of a stretch, so let me review the main types of misinformation you will encounter:

1. False or exaggerated side effects and adverse events.

2. False statements about lack of efficacy.

3. Discrediting a product by attacking business motivations (ex: the new drug is 'just a patent extension ploy').

4. The mysterious 3rd party quote ('a doc in Boondocks said a patient died from spontaneous combustion while on the drug').

How do you combat negative misinformation?

Answer:
Don't get defensive. There is no need, and it may arouse suspicion that perhaps there is credence to the rumors. Don't lose your composure, no matter how angry the misinformation makes you! (Remember Shakespeare's advice about 'not protesting too much...') Defeat the lies with the solid science, likely already in your detail.

Remind us that it is really an insult to the customer to base marketing on misinformation. You can also remind us that you detail based on credible science and what is best for patients, and have no need or desire to fabricate information (you like your job too much!).

Remind us why it is done – usually this happens when another product cannot compete on its merits. This is also an excellent opportunity to point out why your market share is growing.

Even Better Answer:

Strong relationships with your docs:

This is best illustrated by the following story from my own practice. I have an outstanding relationship with company X's representatives and find their drug to be a superior agent and use it preferentially in its class. A competitor rep recently came by to argue that the reps for Drug X are lying about a new study, he further misstated the results and interpretation of this large multi-center trial of Drug X. (I knew for certain he had misstated it because I had participated in the study!). I felt personally angry that he had done this - as my research was insulted, the excellent product was disparaged, and also, my friends were under attack.

I am a psychiatrist, so I can't go too long without mentioning feelings, right? Well, mine was one of anger. Even if I was unfamiliar with the data, I would still feel my friends were maligned. (Like the well-trained shrink I am, I showed no emotion and said 'that's all the time I have, thank you for coming by,' and escorted him out. He left puzzled at my abrupt end to our conversation - must have been something he said…)

4. The Troll at the Bridge (or, the evil gatekeeper…)

One of your most critical tasks will be to consider the gatekeeper staff as customers too, and sell yourself - your credibility and services, to them. Most are genuinely nice individuals, but they are time-pressured people trying to protect their time-pressured bosses. However, some are just determined to abuse the small bit of power they have, and can make access the most challenging part of the day.

When things go south, and a staff member has an agenda (to keep you out), you must be creative and find a way to engage your customer outside the office setting. Lunches or dinners with you and possibly a visiting expert are usually the most effective strategies.

I have reflected on this quite a bit since the last time I was shut-out! I was visiting offices with a rep before a speaker program – 'we have Dr. Farah with us today, author of this and that and Dr. Jones is expecting us to stop by…' the Troll was unimpressed – 'well, just get out before ten minutes go by…' I was told…

Don't take it personally, it happens to the best of us!

1. "No Rep" Policies

Without access, you can't begin to influence prescription habits. Sadly, many offices are banning representatives across the country. It is usually the result of one bad experience, after which, everyone gets painted with the same brush. You are unfortunately (and unfairly) held accountable for the last irresponsible rep to visit.

Like you, I am disappointed at the reactionary stance of banning all reps when one may have been inappropriate. Yet sometimes, an office feels they need to exert control over the sales industry, and bans are instituted. I recently had a discussion with a colleague in our Internal Medicine department who banned all representatives from his clinics, even ones he told me were helpful and provided great service. I asked him why he wanted to ban the *one* group of people we encounter who are always respectful and helpful, ready to share patient care information, took grant applications for our research, provide CME funding for us as well as a generous supply of free medications and services to our patients? What could possibly be gained by denying his staff and patients these resources?

"I feel better knowing I'm not influenced by marketing."

And that was the answer; he traded all the help you offer for a 'feeling.' No logic in that argument. I suggested that if he wasn't savvy enough to tell the difference between a marketing message and credible scientific evidence, he had no business seeing patients. I can't repeat his next comment...

Clearly, he acknowledged your services were an asset, and yes, even he still wanted them. But he needs to get them outside the office setting. View the act of banning reps as a control issue – they feel they have lost control over your access because of the demands of more assertive reps, so they believe stopping all contact is a way of getting control back. Your strategy is to allow them that control: make them aware of what you can offer and be flexible enough to do it on their terms. Does that mean CME's, outside lunches or dinners? Possibly- it means whatever it takes, and the only limits are your creativity.

Again, a solid relationship will transcend this control game. Even if reps are banned, you may learn that some are still getting access. All friends get through, while other reps may not.

2. Information Overload

Physicians more than anyone operate on information overload. Medical data is much like investment-related data, there's plenty out there, the trick is sorting out which pieces are relevant and even critical. When I lecture on antidepressants, I have a slide titled 'Drug Interactions That Matter,' because there are hundreds of theoretical interactions that can occur, but clinicians need to keep in mind just a handful that are dangerous. Many people request a copy of this slide. We experts have done such a thorough job of listing all the rare (and theoretical) dangers that the important ones have been lost in the shuffle.

Reps also present us with a great deal of data, and when I feel overwhelmed by the sheer volume of it, I notice myself editing your details as they progress, tuning in to relevant data, tuning out what will not be critical for my practice. Your task is to find out what is critical to us, and tailor your details to the customer. If you say the same thing from office to office, you are doing too much talking and not enough listening to your customers.

3. The Customer is Wrong

You are an expert on your medications, but most of your customers are not on your speaker panels, did not participate in clinical trials, and they do not write articles relevant to your medication. You may encounter a situation similar to mine on a recent lecture trip: an audience member made the comment that the new medication we were discussing was formulated as a patent extension and had no real value over the meds that were available earlier. He insisted that it was all an economic ploy. The reality is, the parent drug is at least three years away from patent expiration, and his assertions were simply incorrect. Does this remind you of any of your past calls? A doc says something you know to be false, and you need to correct the misperception but don't want to seem disrespectful or embrass the customer.

Handle it like I did: I first let him know that it is a common mistake, as the competition had planted the misinformation and very much wanted him to think this was the case. Then I stated the facts in a very matter-of-fact way – again, reemphasizing that this is what most people think.

What if your efforts are unsuccessful? Instead of tactfully educating the physician about the facts, he or she argues with you, insists that *you* have the facts wrong. If it is critical to patient care, you certainly need to get the issues clarified, and to do so, you must call in reinforcements. You must find an expert or medical liaison that outranks you! Sometimes the customer only listens to the stranger from out of town rather than the one they have the relationship with (a lot like communication after marriage).

4. The Curse of One Bad Experience

A representative at one of my lectures explained a difficult situation: she had an excellent relationship with a physician, their families socialized together frequently, and he was a strong supporter of her medication for hypertension. However, one patient experienced an allergic reaction to a medication, and her drug was one of the three being taken at the time. The relationship is still strong, professionally and personally, but the physician never used the product again, even though two other products could have been solely or partly responsible for the bad experience. What should she do?

Continue to be a positive presence, a resource and partner in patient care. Remind the doc that this is a rare occurrence that can happen with any medication, and slowly move them back into the comfort zone of prescribing. In this situation, you readjust your timeline and expect that usage will not follow for several weeks.

Once the worst has happened, prescribing may never reach the comfort zone again, but ironically it should be there immediately: The odds of a second extremely rare event are even less likely.

5. Cost Arguments

A colleague recently asked for my input on two cases: both patients responded beautifully to the therapy he had chosen, as both were severely depressed individuals who had only partially responded to their antidepressants. They were given a new medication for narcolepsy. It promotes normal wakefulness, and when given to these depressed patients (who were sleeping excessively, even on antidepressants) was described as 'a miracle cure.' They were back to baseline after months of depression and job absence. They knew the usage was 'off-label' but benefit far outweighed risk. They were responding well, but despite this, they both stopped the new drug within two months of therapy due to the cost. What better response can you expect from a drug than the label 'miracle cure?' Still, the drugs were discontinued and a generic stimulant was used without much benefit. As reps, you have heard similar stories too often.

Nothing kills the dialogue faster, or has become such a definitive dead-end for a rep as a doc saying "well, it's an expensive drug." It can seem that no matter what advantages a product will have for a patient, it will be accepted as a limited-use drug if cost becomes the predominant issue. The psychology behind this is partly related to the fact that insured patients come in with a variety of prescription plans, all limiting the coverage of some drugs, and most with a 'tiered' co-pay system for medications in a particular class. It has become impossible for the prescriber to keep up with which plans cover which medications in which territories. The situation is further complicated by the fact that some drugs are covered if prescribed by a specialist but not a primary care provider! Unable to keep up, most physicians simply avoid products that they deem 'too expensive.' Why prescribe what will not be filled? (Some patients call and complain when a covered drug's co-pay is $30, rather than $5 or $10).

But what is *too* expensive? We all have priorities for spending. One of my friends can't understand why I pay so much for season basketball tickets while I have trouble understanding how he can pay several hundred dollars for a bottle of wine he'll never drink. We all have some passion whose value is disconnected from the price. And health is like that, isn't it? You can't really put a price on it, can you?

It turns out that your customer has some very specific ideas about the price of medications. When asked 'how much is too much?' a focus group of primary care doctors responded 'what illness are we talking about?' For life threatening illness, it was a green light no matter the cost, for subacute problems and chronic illness, cost was heavily considered. Here are some examples of the scenarios discussed:

Case 1: A patient responds to a brand antihypertensive but his co-pay is $30 a month. A generic is $7. He requests a change. Most physicians would change to generic unless there is some protective value for the current agent - such as renal protection, or antiarrhythmic properties more reliable with, or specific to, the brand.

Case 2: A patient responds to an antidepressant that costs $65 a month, but generic amitriptyline is $6. No physician surveyed would change the prescription due to the side effects of this generic and its toxicity in overdose. The risks far outweighed the benefit of cost savings.

You see how this simple question can get quickly complicated – but the critical factors are acuity and perceived seriousness of disease state, additional benefits of the brand that further justify use, and risks associated with the cheaper alternative therapies.

What if really pressed for a number, above which a maintenance drug was deemed too costly to prescribe? The consensus number was (averaged to be:) $90. This magical figure is under the psychological barrier of $100. While a drug under $50 was considered cost-friendly, and cost was no reason to limit use, the $51-$90 range was a different matter. Here it was up to the rep to justify cost with the drug's advantages.

Summary of the Cost Quandary:

- Fairly or unfairly, cost concerns kill dialogue.

- Medications under $50 are generally prescribed feely.

- Medications over $90 are avoided unless certain circumstances warrant use (cancer treatment, no alternative therapy, severe toxicity of generics options, or dramatic life-changing results are the most common reasons).

- **The bulk of your work will be on behalf of products $51 - $90 in cost.**

Summary:

The Major Obstacles to Getting Your Message Out Are:

- Time pressured customers
- Customers with their minds already made up
- Negative misinformation about your product
- Gatekeeper power games
- No-Rep policies
- Excessive information overloading customers
- Customers who have their facts wrong
- Limited, but negative, product experiences
- Cost objections

The majority of these hurdles can be overcome by developing a strong and mutually beneficial relationship with your physician customers. Relationship will lead to access, known credibility, and support.

For the hundredth time in as many days, I don't need a free pen!!!

Chapter 9

Relationship Based Selling

When people ask me if there is one key, or one essential secret to selling to physicians, I answer with one word: **relationship**. Building and enjoying a relationship with your docs is the best way to gain instant access and quality time. Your educational skills will then be fully utilized to help the patients in your community.

However, there is a catch. Remember the book, *Catch 22*? The airman wanted out of World War II, so he asked the military doctor to declare him insane. The only problem was, as the doc explained, to want *in* the war is insane. The very fact that he wanted out proved his sanity. That was the catch, and it has become a metaphor for any situation defined by its self-defeating paradox.

Your catch goes something like this: in order to be an effective salesperson, to gain limitless access and time, you have to build a relationship. But as relationships progress, they tend to get friendlier and then professional barriers break down. It becomes harder to sell when you realize you are trying to sell a friend, not a customer. In fact, you may find a complete shift in the dynamic has occurred – you are now embarrassed and shy about trying to talk product, when at first you were only nervous about personal discussions!

You have probably already found yourself in this situation in your career – you may have attempted to detail a doc who says, "Let's not talk about that stuff, how was the game? How are your kids doing?" It's as if they said "let's catch up on everything *but* business." Since many of you are recalling relationships in which this is currently the case, let's talk about how to approach this challenging situation:

1. Change the focus of the detail so that it is very specific to that doctor's needs. If you know your customer's practice well, you can use that knowledge to detail beyond the level of the latest marketing emphasis. For example, a rep recently helped me explore the safety of his product when combined with a new drug for Parkinson's disease. It was safe, and two patients soon benefited, but only because the rep had the awareness to start a dialogue about the neurological profiles of our patients. He started the conversation about our specific needs and opened a door neither of us had seen before.

2. Detail the impersonal by making it personal. For example, a friend of mine (who started out as just another rep, new to me only a year ago), was given marching orders to 'show Dr. Farah the new marketing study.' Now, when she came by, I was interested in how her pregnancy was going and wanted to see the ultrasound shots of the little guy. The last thing on my mind was a study I had already read months before when it was newly published. The best approach here is NOT 'forget my pregnancy, we have to go over this new study,' but rather, to go ahead and enjoy the personal time, and then ask: 'please look at this with me, it is our new study, help me understand what is most important to cover in details with other docs.' I am still a friend, not insulted by the business-only approach, and I am asked as a friend to help relay information about the study. The effect is still the same, doc reviews study, but the scenario is much better. As I reflect on the study with you, I am getting much more out of it than if you simply read parts of it to me.

Avoiding the Catch

This is an art you will practice throughout your career – a professional relationship that is enhanced, not compromised by friendliness. First, operate somewhat as a psychotherapist might, not allowing too much personal disclosure. Some is fine, but too much will lead you far from business. Even if a customer shares information that may be sensitive, don't follow them down that path. If they pry, brush off the questions with quick dismissive statements and get back on track.

The second rule is to encourage the doc to lead the product discussion – let your friend tell you how it is going with the medication and ask for permission to quote the positives and dramatic benefits they tout.

A step further, and what will lead to the best outcome of all in relationship-based selling, involves enlisting the customer as your agent in product promotion. How is this possible? Here are some examples from my own practice:

I find drug X to be the best agent for patients and use it preferentially in the class. I frequently speak on behalf of drug X, and my rep recently asked me to help spread the word about its benefits. He has arranged:

- Roundtable and lunch meetings in the community to get the message out.

- Support from medical affairs to help with publications.

- Review of data with him and other reps, and discussions about the territory and its needs.

This rep has personalized our encounters, but you can see, they are all business, and mutually beneficial.

Summary:

- The success of your mission depends on your relationships with your docs.

- Relationships can become too personal, and effective detailing then becomes very challenging.

- To avoid this trap, be less divulging of personal information and maintain professional boundaries.

- Transform personal relationships into productive business ones by using your knowledge of the customer to better meet their needs.

- Enlist your physician friends as agents in product promotion.

Detail in da' Bronx....

'We tried askin' for the business real nice, Doc, but not this time.'

Chapter 10

The Comfort Zone of Prescribing

A prescription is written because the physician believes that a particular medication is in the patient's best interest. We tend to prescribe mostly from our 'comfort zone,' meaning the agents we use most often are ones we know well, including side effects as well as benefits, and we feel confident the outcome will be positive. Further, if an outcome or side effect is untoward, we know we can handle that too. This is true with products as common and safe as gastric reflux agents, as well as with chemotherapeutic agents, inevitably causing certain side effects and known to be poorly tolerated. Thus, an agent can have an extensive and unpleasant side effect profile, and higher risks associated with its use, but we can still feel comfortable prescribing it if the patient needs it. However, if we are uncomfortable using a product, no matter how well tolerated it is, it falls to the last choice of the class.

This makes sense on the surface, that prescribers need to sense a certain degree of comfort about a product in order to use it freely, but what does this really mean? And how can you facilitate the necessary transition of an unknown product, or even an avoided one, to that zone of frequent usage?

In order to take this abstract concept of 'comfort' and make it useful in your day to day encounters, we'll start by looking at the data:

What makes a physician feel comfortable about a product?

1. Knowing it will work – reliably.
2. Knowing it is safe.
3. Knowing how to manage untoward effects.
4. Gaining experience in challenging cases.

And finally:

5. Rep support!

These five most commonly given answers are no surprise. Firstly, in order to feel completely at ease prescribing your drug, efficacy must be unquestioned. Studies and FDA approval may herald a drug's reliability and known efficacy, but the issue is whether this data reflects the reality of the customer's clinical practice. Is that reliability consistent with his or her experience?

The concept of reliable efficacy can be a particular challenge with new advancements such as Alzheimer's agents, because the mindset of effectiveness must be reset. No longer can you discuss cure, or full response to medication, but better management, delayed nursing home placement, and slower disease progression. The message is still one of efficacy, but the measures of success require new language.

All of your customers are concerned with safety, but few are as sharply focused on this issue as the pediatricians. This is their top concern, so be mindful of this when you detail them. For other doctors, it is a close second behind reliable efficacy, and most elaborated that it was not listed first because they 'assume that an agent past Phase II trials and FDA-approval is safe."

Catastrophic adverse events, no matter how rare, will stay at the forefront of the customer's mind, and obviously impact usage. For example, consider the following scenario: 600,000 patients took an agent in a one-year period, and three developed liver failure (one died, one recovered, one received a transplant). Though tragic, these three cases represent a tiny fraction of all individuals exposed to the drug in trails and post launch usage. No matter that the odds of such an event are approximately 0 .000005%, no physician surveyed said they would consider usage of this hypothetical agent.

Regarding response 4, the first time I used a newer narcolepsy agent, it was in a catatonic (essentially mute and frozen) individual (with severe psychotic depression). He refused antidepressants, and convulsive therapy, so I had little choice but to try something innovative, and of course 'off-label.' He was 89 and had a pacemaker – and was such a complicated case that none of my colleagues would accept him as a patient! He was given a new narcolepsy-approved drug for depression, and he responded, actually quite well and with no discernable side effects. After such a complicated and risky first case, imagine how comfortable I was using the drug in a 32 year-old medically healthy patient!

Finally, and most importantly, your support is necessary. Your confidence in your drug's efficacy and your knowledge of side effects and management will be what we fall back on until we see these attributes for ourselves. I often tell severely depressed patients to borrow some of my hope until theirs comes back. A hopeless individual can sense that I am confident that they will respond to treatment and this infused hope can be critical in facilitating their recovery through the initial days of treatment, when suicide risk may be greatest.

In certain illnesses, the majority of patient change occurs as a result of the relationship they have with their doctor or therapist. As in your mission, change in your customer's mindset is facilitated through your relationship. Make it one of confidence and support, and when this is a consistent sincere message, we can move your product to the zone of comfort.

When you close, as discussed in the next chapter, consider using the language of this comfort.

Summary:

- Prescriptions are written from a zone of comfort.

- Your job involves moving your product into that zone of free usage.

- When a doctor is comfortable using your drug, they understand the benefits, risks, and the side effects and how to deal with them.

- Docs usually feel very comfortable with a drug after using it in certain higher-risk situations.

- Rep support is critical to comfort level, particularly soon after a launch.

'It appears he's chasing the physician for a signature...'

Chapter 11

The Close

The most effective close I recall involved a rep who showed me a new study involving his product that actually decreased hospital days when used in Bipolar patients. This study pertained directly to my practice. I was so impressed with the data that I said "I can't wait to try it on Mr. Jones, he's been here for two weeks and won't stabilize." Then I realized that the rep must have done a great job, I closed for him!

Your goal is not to make the close, but to make the close unnecessary. If you do an excellent job of convincing me that your product is the best choice when indicated, and at the end of our discussion I have no questions and feel using it will be a great service to the patient, future usage is understood. It would be silly and counterproductive to ask for a commitment of use (in fact, it may make me wonder how credible the information I just heard was if such a request is necessary!) Future product use should follow as the logical outcome to your detail. When reps do their job in such a superior fashion, they may find the doc closing for them, as in my example.

If your management instructs that a verbal commitment of some sort is needed to finalize your details, then try these approaches:

- *I want you to feel completely comfortable trying Drug X, so do you have any other questions or concerns I can answer?*
- *Is there any other data I can show you to make you more comfortable using Drug X?*
- *I know you're comfortable using Drug X after all we've discussed, is there anything I can provide as far as information or studies?*

You get the idea, a gentle, reassuring close, not a demand. Still, if you find it necessary to ask for "X number of new patients," turn this into an exercise you will monitor:

- I hope you are comfortable using Drug X on the next few patients - when I come back in three weeks I'd love to hear your experiences.

The real message is 'your opinions are important and I need to know your experience with my product.' The close really doesn't sound all that different, but the shift in premise is profound. You are no longer saying 'You owe me the next ten patients, I need the business,' you are saying 'Your input is valuable, please educate me on how my product can help your patients.'

That's a win-win close.

Summary:

- Strive to make the close unnecessary, the natural conclusion to your excellent detail.

- If you must ask for commitment of use, make it an exercise to be followed over time.

- Use the language associated with comfort of product usage.

- If you have succeeded you will have moved your product to that comfort zone of frequent and hesitation-free usage.

Chapter 12

What Really Changes Prescription Habits

I decided to write this book during my first year of practice out of residency. I was impressed with the knowledge and kindness of the representatives that were calling on me, and despite their skills, I was amazed when I analyzed my prescription habits. I used drug X as my first-line agent for depression, drug Z first-line for psychosis, then drug Q if drug Z fails. I was predictable, and my habits were fixed. They rarely changed. Why should they? Patients were getting well with my decisions, and I had more referrals than slots to put them in - my habits were working just fine for the patients and the practice.

My reps kept coming by, those that represented the first line choices and those that didn't. They had very persuasive arguments as to why their antidepressant or antipsychotic should be my number one option, but despite their visits, for the most part, my habits remained intact. However, over time, a few of my prescription habits did change. The point is, so few details really had their desired intent, and I wanted to examine why. Why did one rep's information change my habits and result in hundreds of prescriptions for her product instead of a previous choice?

At a seminar, a representative asked probably the most interesting question I have ever heard on this topic: *Dr. Farah, as a psychiatrist, how do you facilitate a habit change in your patients?* Her question was right on target – and when I reflected on patient change as a model for prescription habit change, I realized that the basic tenants are the same:

Of course, in psychiatry, we are very interested in what motivates change – and when examined in the clinical setting (i.e., why one patient relapses and another stays clean, or why one schizophrenic stays on the medication while another is non-complaint), the most important factor is:

The relationship they have with their provider. No kidding!

It All Starts with Relationship

The therapeutic alliance – or the doctor-patient relationship is the most important factor in facilitating patient change, and it has been suggested this accounts for 85% of the change that occurs in our profession! Take this lesson to heart – my chances of helping a patient change are most directly related to the alliance I have with them. The chances you can affect change in your customers is dependent on the same type of alliance. If you want to change a habit, focus on the relationship.

I was reminded of that first year out of residency by a rep who told me that during that time, I 'wrote for more of drug Q than anyone else in the entire southeastern US.' He went on, 'you were the number one prescriber of my drug here, and number two in the nation.' I reflected on that time and in response, I said one name, 'LeeAnne.' She was my rep then, and perhaps the best I can recall. She had cultivated a great relationship and had become a member of our treatment team. The product was great, and still is, but the rep was the one who propelled it to record use and the resultant patient benefits through her relational selling.

Instilling the Desire for Change:

It's a worn out cliché, but usually true. If a person lacks the desire for change, none will occur. As clinicians, often our first task is instilling that very desire. If I simply tell a patient what to do, they may ignore the advice, or may come back and report 'I tried what you said, and it didn't work,' thereby avoiding the whole issue of whether they want the change at all. Simply telling someone to use your product, like telling a patient how to live their life, is a set-up for disaster.

Think of your own experiences, and who has inspired you to change, or take action in a certain direction. How did they inspire you? Chances are they didn't demand something of you, they persuaded you that it was in your best interest.

Your role as a rep is to help us see why your agent is the best service we can provide to the patient. Is it better tolerated? Will I get fewer phone calls about side effects? Patient benefit is your main approach in this scenario. Telling me I am doing something wrong will make me defensive. Telling me that patients will benefit will get my attention.

What if the doctor is already satisfied with their first line agent, and asks you, "Why should I change?"

Think about the sales dilemma a different way – *How can I motivate this doctor to use drug Z? How will it make life easier for the doc, and better for the patient?*

Visiting experts can make a huge difference. If you have the opportunity to arrange lunches or dinners with speakers and key clients, do so. Also, in this tough situation, try detailing with the awareness that you draw no conclusions. What? Yes, draw no conclusions! Let *us* draw them, we may eventually think they are our own ideas, and you know how we love those.

Consider this example: rep says, "our drug has no sexual side effects and all the others have a 30-70% rate. It is obvious that ours should be first-line." Or "our product is unique, this study shows a placebo rate of sexual side effects."

Yes, end it there, don't overstate the obvious or draw the conclusion for us, it will be counterproductive when the customer is resistant to change.

Summary:

- To really facilitate a change in prescribing habits, start with a solid relationship.

- Don't tell someone to change, instill the desire for change.

- Convince your docs that your product is in the best interest of the patient.

- Convince your docs that using your product will make their lives easier.

- When you draw the conclusions for us, you are lecturing us - when we draw the conclusions, we are more likely to remember and use the data.

- Reflect on your life, and what inspires you to take action or change a habit.

'You have cat-scratch fever…'

Chapter 13

The Top Mistakes that Reduce Market Share

After residency, I was briefly in a practice with a group of physicians whose senior partners were, let's say, interesting. My favorite was referred to as 'The Script Nazi' because if a patient was late for the appointment, he was likely to refuse to see them and send them home with the phrase *'No script for you! Come back one month!'* Another was infamous for once falling asleep while in session with a patient, and when roused and confronted with this fact, he told the patient *'What do you expect, you are boring!'* The most vocal of them would frequently explode at the staff for no justifiable reason, was equally rude to the patients, and refused to do hospital consultations, dumping the work load onto me, the most junior partner. Interestingly, despite the handicaps posed by their interpersonal skills, they were all brilliant doctors. How they accepted reps is another chapter...

I discussed with my father how disappointed I was to realize there was so very little to learn about the medical business from such a crew, and his wisdom was right on target: *sometimes you learn a lot from seeing how not to do the job.*

Here are the ways **not** to do your job:

1. Inserting Yourself Before the Patients

Perhaps the worst mistake a rep can make is placing his or her needs above patient needs. I recall a rep that was banned from a particular clinic in which one of the exam rooms doubled as a sample closet. The nurse asked the rep to leave this room so she could administer an injection to her patient. The rep said he would as soon as he finished stocking his samples. The nurse was irritated, but waited for him to finish. The clinic director, who overheard the exchange, was not as forgiving. The rep and the samples left, and to this day, he has not been allowed back.

This rep made the most critical of mistakes because he lost sight of his mission. We are on the same team – physicians and reps are both motivated by excellent patient care. Tasks can always wait, patient needs should not.

I recently spent the day with a rep visiting offices and discussing the advantages of a new antidepressant. Steve (the rep) parked as far away as he could at each office, and by the fourth office, I was a little curious – "are we trying to walk a mile so we can skip the gym this afternoon, or perhaps you're afraid someone will add the hundredth ding to your Taurus?" No, he said, he was just saving the closer spaces for the patients.

2. Not Respecting Time Constraints

Today was one of the busiest days of the year. The inpatient ward was full, I had two lengthy meetings, and several consultations. But two reps did call on me – we'll call one Roderick and the other Kristel. Now, Kristel is an excellent rep who realized I was swamped. Rather than try to detail me, she took a few seconds to arrange a late lunch for us to discuss her new product and the related formulary quest at our hospital. Roderick, whom you will hear more about later, simply kept trying to chat with me, while I was in the hall, in a patient care area, and my pager was going off, and the staff kept asking questions - you get the idea. I gave the nursing director, Abby, the high-sign and soon I was rescued. She led him away. His information was probably good, but I simply didn't have the time he kept trying to take.

All of your customers are under time pressure. One exercise I encourage in rep training is to abbreviate the entire detail to thirty seconds. Then to ten! What is the most important message about your product? What are the two things you want me to remember after you leave? Can you say it in three sentences? Of course you want more time, but make small bits count.

Reps who are intrusive and try to take time that is unavailable will defeat themselves. Even when Roderick tried to tell me valuable product information, I had no choice but to keep ignoring him, as I was simply pulled in too many directions. The message, however helpful, was lost. Make the effort to find our best times, and if a cold call is not working, follow Kristel's example and simply reschedule.

3. Sharing the Numbers

Unless your customers have been living on Mars for the past two decades, they should be fully aware that your company tracks prescription data. It is the universal system for monitoring product growth and your specific impact, but also, national prescription patterns or 'market share' are invaluable clinical information.

If a product is number one in its class, that tells us that without a doubt, it is effective and patients are benefiting. If a product gets no traction despite marketing and a team of excellent salespeople, it indicates the product is the problem. Your customers find it very useful to hear about prescription trends because it allows us to compare our impression with that of thousands of doctor across the country. The data shared at advisory board meetings is particularly useful in this regard.

However, it is unacceptable to share a clinician's personal prescription data, nor should you divulge the data of others in the community. You may even be asked by a physician to show you 'the numbers,' or even the data related to other physicians. Though this may seem like an excellent opportunity to open the door to rapport and discuss products, it is really a trap door. When business concerns are the focus of your discussion, patient care is secondary. Your focus must always be patient first, and if you are doing your job well in this regard, numbers will follow.

I have been asked, "What should I do when a doc says 'I know you have my numbers, let me see them!'" An excellent question - well, the first rule is, if someone asks you something that is frankly none of their business, (and telling them exactly that will damage your relationship) then it is perfectly fine to politely not answer – here are some responses that may help you out of that jam-

- *The data is not stored in my computer. I don't have access to that information here.*

- *All I have seen is data by zip code, so I don't know individual clinician data.*

- *I don't pay attention to that – I focus on hearing from my doctors what is working for the patients. If the patients are getting better, I'm sure the numbers will reflect that.*

- *Do I look like the Gallup Poll Agency!!!* (Just kidding, don't try that approach...)

4. Talking Business

I have only banned one rep in my life from the office. Well, I didn't really do it, I had an office manager do the dirty work and tell him I didn't care to see him that day or in the future. He walked in already very frustrated, and he didn't hide his anger at the fact that I rarely used his medication (in fact, I don't recall if I ever used it while he was my rep). He kept insisting that he "got nowhere in this territory" and that his manager was insisting he work on *my* prescriptions. He spent the whole time telling me that neglecting his drug was terrible for his business, his territory, his ranking, his company – but never said why it might be a good option for the patients. His focus was completely the opposite of what it should have been. I made sure our meeting that day was brief, but I would still like to have a relationship with a rep from his company. (This is an excellent opportunity for cross coverage, as the company could send a rep who presents clinical information instead of business problems.)

This example is not only instructive because the all-business focus will turn off your customers, but frustration and anger have no place in your calls.

5. Negative-Only Details

I know a great rep who has educated our staff on her excellent product, but every time I get time with her, she only talks about the competitors. She tells me drug X has no efficacy, drug Z causes too many side effects, and drug Y does something horrible in phase 1 trials (I think she said rats spontaneously combusted, but I usually stop her before the details). The main problems with this approach are firstly, negativity leaves a negative impression. Secondly, while she disparages competitor drugs, I am thinking of the numerous patients doing quite well on each of them. Third – your customers may wonder why you choose not to talk positively about your drug. The 'use my drug because everyone else is terrible' strategy is the wrong approach, and was ranked quite low by specialists in the following study:

When asked to rank the following detail approaches from most desirable to least:
-   Most desirable: Your drug over 75% of the detail, compared to others when relevant.
-   Second most desirable approach: Your drug only, no mention of competition.
-   Third: some side effects of competition, over 50% positive information about your drug.

- Least desirable approach: Discuss side effects or negative aspects of competitors only.

The most striking finding of this small survey was that docs consistently requested that you stick to a positive message about your drug. Your customers would rather not hear about the competition if all you have to share are negative comments.

6. Too Familiar Too Soon

It takes time and effort to build a mutually successful relationship with your customers. There are four reps who currently have my private phone number, are welcome anytime on my ward or in our clinic without an appointment, and if they call and ask me to speak at a lunch or dinner program on just an hour's notice, I will (provided there's not a Wake Forest game at the same time). They have done the work necessary, and now I rely on them to help elevate the level of patient care.

Then there is Roderick. You remember him from topic 2, *Time Constraints*. Roderick is not his real name, in fact, I didn't make an effort to learn his name. He was present at the tail end of another visit from two of the reps. I assume he got a glimpse of the relationship they had and began to emulate it. The main problem was, this was our first meeting! I was trying to finish my work as he stood there chatting and interrupting my charting. *Well, kind of busy now, is there another time you can come by?* He said he'd wait. So he did. Again, in a patient care area, just hanging out and distracting me. I was rescued by one of our directors, Jeni, who saw my pained expression and grabbed the rep by the arm and invited him for coffee – downstairs. She explained some of our protocol to him.

Now, most guys would rather go off with a pretty girl for coffee than watch me do chart-work, but he was lead away because he decided to be too familiar with me, not only too soon, but at the worst time of the day.

What doesn't make sense about this story? I mentioned he witnessed two other reps just moments before, so why wasn't I too busy to see them? This demonstrates the power of a solid relationship. The two reps I mentioned, Jana and Mike, are considered part of our treatment team. They provide meds to our patients, education to our staff, and clinical information and resources to me. Interrupting hospital rounds to meet with them and get questions answered about their agent *is* good patient care.

7. Being Defined by Your Critics

My brother is one of those political types you never hear of. I suppose the terms for them are 'strategists,' or 'operatives.' In fact, he does not want you to know his name (which is David Farah) or certainly not the names of those who call for campaign advice (such as....well, I don't really know who they are). What he does tell them is the worst mistake a politician can make? Being defined by your critics! If your opponent throws mud and you let it stick, it will soon define you. No-one wants to start their argument on the defensive. And he reminds us that a vast number of people are 'not really paying attention.' To them, the news is background noise, and if they hear 'Senator Jones was cleared of fraud charges,' what they remember of this sound-byte two days later is the name 'Jones' and the word 'fraud.' He also advises conservatives that 'at least 95% of the people writing stories about you for TV and print media are not voting for you!'

This political advice is important for the rep as well. We expect your competition to compare their drug to yours, and of course, theirs will emerge in the more favorable light. Are these comparisons always 'fair and balanced?' Probably not. When your competition defines you, it will most often be in a negative way. That's why you should not let the discussion of your drug's side effects or disadvantages be the last word. Ask us what the competition is saying, and use those remarks as a springboard for discussion. Don't let your enemies define you. Answer the negativism and defeat it with fact.

8. The Magical Disappearing Rep!

As we established in chapter 6, we expect a certain amount of consistent contact with our reps. I recall the last time I saw a wonderful, very helpful and enthusiastic rep for lets say, drug Q. We were at a national meeting and had a wonderful dinner with spouses. (I even paid! I didn't want her in any trouble for expensing our partners' dinners, and was glad to do this, as our business relationship was very solid.) However, when we got home, she magically disappeared! About four months later a new rep came by and explained that my friend had been reassigned to a new area and she would take her place. Imagine what happened to the market share of her product? It was not used in our hospital or clinic much at all over those four months - not because of some petty spite, but because we needed rep input. We depended on our rep for guidance in using and switching patients to this new product. The new rep has to start all over, building rapport, building relationship, and becoming a trusted asset.

There is a right way to exit – simply come by and explain what is going on with realignment and introduce us to the new rep. Call on us together for a while if feasible. When the most critical person for product support disappears, so does market share. But the most important thing I learned was to go ahead and let the rep pay when at a five-star restaurant…

9. Lack of Follow Through

You may recall an example I used in an earlier chapter, when I discussed avoiding a product because I was so unclear on its mechanism of action. My Medline searches were not giving me the answers I needed. This may seem petty - if a drug works, it works, right? Sure, but in psychiatry, mechanisms are perhaps more important to the prescriber. For example, the average bipolar patient leaves the hospital with over four prescriptions for psychoactive drugs! I asked the rep to find some literature of exactly where this drug blocks receptors and to what extent. He said a Medical Science Liaison would contact me soon. That person never got the message, or perhaps they did, and didn't follow through. Two months have gone by since the request. I have written for the drug only five times since then.

Let's face it, you have spoiled us: we expect rapid and accurate follow through on our requests. You are held to the very high standard you have set for yourselves. Back to my example: I received a voice mail yesterday from a colleague who reports the drug I've avoided is a 'miracle cure' for Mr. Jones, who is now hospitalized on my ward. (Mr. Jones is paranoid, and when asked who is going to harm him, and what he is concerned about, he insists you too are in on the conspiracy and returns the question: *You tell me!* He says, *You are one of them!*) I was grateful for the information and started the drug. I worry about how many other patients may have found a 'miracle cure' if I had been using the drug that I avoided. To best help patients, we depend on our reps as our partners in care.

10. The Bumbling Detail

The product detail is your main tool for affecting changes in prescription habits. Doing it well is expected and taken for granted by your customers. Doing it poorly will cost you credibility and damage the work you have already done. If you have a set of complex scientific points to convey, rehearse them! Better to sound a little scripted and get it right than to fumble through it and erode confidence.

Here's an example from my speaking experience: a common question when I lecture about an SRI antidepressant is "tell us about safety in pregnancy?" I hear this question almost every time I talk about depression (likely because eighty percent of antidepressants are prescribed to women), so I learned early on to have a well-stated and accurate answer ready. Just for comparison, I asked a visiting speaker this very question about a different antidepressant:

"Doctor X, is this drug safe for pregnant patients and their fetuses?" – He said:

> "We think so, I mean, we use them and I know there are studies for post-partem depression and PMS so we see women on them when pregnant and we also see women on antipsychotics sometimes too."

Huh? Perhaps he too had researched this topic, but he certainly didn't articulate a sure knowledge of it. The complex and important question was left virtually unanswered – in fact, the colleague next to me said "we sometimes see women on cocaine when pregnant, but that doesn't mean it's safe."

- Here's my standard (and yes, rehearsed) answer:

> Depression during pregnancy is a major concern, as it puts an infant at risk for low birth weight and possibly other complications. So it is important to treat the depression through pregnancy and to continue the antidepressant after delivery to prevent post-partmen depression. The risk factors for depression during pregnancy include a past history, a history of affective symptoms when on oral contraceptives, and social stressors, such as lack of partner support or

ambivalence about the pregnancy. The FDA categorizes all SRI antidepressants as category C, which means birth defects are not expected, but controlled studies are unavailable. As with any drug, no exposure is of course the best option - unless benefit outweighs risk. In this case, the benefit can be tremendous and the risk is, thus far, from published data and clinical experience, not really a factor – there is a tremendous amount of data about fluoxetine exposure in the first trimester. Over 1500 infants were exposed to this SRI and there was no increase in the base rate of expected birth defects. The next most commonly used drug in pregnancy, as far as documented cases, is citalopram, and again, no evidence has emerged that it is teratogenic. It is also worth mentioning that children who were exposed to antidepressants of all types in-utero have been studied through preschool and show no signs of developmental or neurological problems.

You can speak extemporaneously and still be rehearsed and therefore extremely accurate.

11. The Non-Stop Detail

I was a visiting faculty guest at a lunch roundtable last week, and the docs and I were having a productive discussion about the NCAA basketball tournament. We talked product too, and discussed many other clinical issues and products other than our sponsor's. It was going well, but the rep was too aggressive, and kept changing the subject to his product. He said important things, but forgot that I was there to carry the ball, and it really became annoying to the docs as well as to me. There were important brackets to discuss! Don't feel the need to detail non-stop. Details are most effective when they are conversational, and like any conversation, are least interesting when they are forced.

Summary:

Do Not –

- Put your needs above patient needs,

- Ignore time constraints,

- Share prescription data,

- Talk only business and neglect product and patient care,

- Detail with only negative statements about your competition,

- Act too familiar with your customers before the relationship allows,

- Let your critics define your product,

- Disappear without a trace – send and support your replacement,

- Fall down on the job of follow-through,

- Fumble a detail - rehearse so you speak thoughtfully and carefully,

- And, do not use the detail to pressure a customer and don't allow the detail to crowd out dialogue.

'This drug is for Social Phobia...'

Part III

The Next Level

There are reps who bring samples to the practice, and there are reps who bring value to the practice.

Pat Gibbons, R.N.

Chapter 14

The Value Mindset

In order to be a trusted member of each treatment team in your territory, a valuable asset to patient care, and not just another rep competing for the same small slice of time, you need to strive for the following goal:

Bring **value** to every call.

Every encounter with a customer is an opportunity to enhance that practice of medicine through your excellent teaching and service.

First – you must be grounded in the Value Mindset.

This initial step is simply realizing that you don't have a job - you have a professional career. You are a skilled professional with a knowledge base that only you and your few colleagues share. I have visited with too many reps who start our visit by apologizing for the encounter – *sorry to take your time,* or *sorry to bother you...* are all too common introductions. Guess what – we *need* your input, we *want* your educational skills and your information is vital in our clinics, so don't feel the need to apologize.

Of course you should be mindful of our time, and of the rules of confidentiality and etiquette that apply to medical settings, but accept that you are a needed professional too. Even if making a cold call, make it with the confidence that you offer what no one else can – and what it takes a professional to deliver: medical education.

Confidence is the first part of the mindset. The second part is delivering a consistently solid message, with the same passion and enthusiasm from office to office. Like the performer who hits different stages with the same enthusiasm, you must visit numerous clinics and deliver your message with passion.

I have seen nearly every home basketball game at Wake Forest for ten years now. Under a previous coach, the team was infamous for playing to the level of the competition. If they played a top-five team, they played like a top-five team, and if they played a terrible team, well, you get the idea. Under the current coach, things are much better. They play like a top-five team every night out. They have a winning mindset, something the commentators call 'swagger' every time they hit the court. You too can hit the field with the same confidence each time out.

If you are distracted, or bogged down by personal issues, or even if you need more time to prepare for your calls, then take the time off to get ready. Part of the value mindset is not making mistakes that hurt your mission. Take the day to regroup, and tell your manager that Dr. Farah gave you a note...

Summary:

- Strive to bring real **value** to every call you make.

- Realize that you are a skilled professional, not a salesperson.

- Approach your career with confidence.

- Deliver a consistent, helpful message.

- Deliver it with the passion that comes from knowing you are contributing to the health of your community.

Chapter 15

Bringing Value to Every Call

Is it really possible to bring real value to every customer encounter? Is this just one of those clichés that's much easier said than done? It may seem an unreachable goal, but it is possible, and four representatives that visit our facilities fit this description. Sure, there are more casual visits when they just stop by to say hello, or see if we have any pressing needs, but when they are making their usual rounds, they are anything but usual reps.

The last time Mike called on me, we discussed the metabolism of his product (as I had a patient with liver disease on his agent), he then introduced me to a fellow rep in a nearby territory who was interested in my speaker programs, and he arranged an in-service for our nursing staff. In one visit, he was able to help the patient we discussed, help my business development by arranging the lecture in a nearby community, and arrange education for our staff. I meet several reps who may accomplish only one of these per year!

Charles stopped by this week as well, he helped me prepare for a lecture by calling Medical Affairs and getting a report on his drug's effect on sleep architecture, and provided me with a liquid form of this product for a Hospice patient unable to swallow pills. Again, in one visit, he helped the patient and helped me speak about new scientific data on the lecture circuit.

How can these examples become reality for you?

1. Do the homework – find out exactly what your customer needs!

2. Focus on the new data – we all strive to be at the cutting edge. I have heard reps complain when they are not allowed to officially share all the great new information they have until a product is approved and launched, but those delays are for your protection. Use the time wisely to study new data and indications to more effectively spread the word when you can.

3. Focus on your customer's support staff – they need education as well, and the value you provide to them is valuable to me.

4. Be creative!!!! Do whatever it takes to contribute.

Summary:

- Approach your calls with the value mindset – know you are a professional bringing value to other professionals.

- If you believe your product is the best option, then approach us with that confidence and be passionate about your convictions.

- Strive to make *every* encounter with your docs an opportunity to bring real value to the practice.

- The value mindset, like a winning mindset, will keep you focused on the fact that each encounter is critical.

- There are no wasted visits, only opportunities.

- Don't be shy, ask the docs and staff how you can enhance each practice and the care of patients.

Chapter 16

Get Invited Back

In every practice, every clinic and hospital, there are representatives who are always welcome, and enjoy a standing invitation. They have unquestioned and unobstructed access. Yes, even in some 'no rep' offices. I have already listed the few names that can enter our clinic anytime, without appointments, and get quality time with our physicians and nurse practitioners. It seems no matter what the demands of the day are, we carve out the necessary time for these excellent reps.

One particular morning I was very busy on our inpatient psychiatric unit trying to finish rounds before an administrative meeting. Several patients needed to be seen, when a rep approached our ward's door. We let him through and I spent time with him. Colin is another rep who is such an asset to our practice that we take the time to allow for his education. We rely on his support for accurate care, and that day, his information on loading of mood stabilizer medications helped a Bipolar patient improve. (Sure, I missed an important meeting, but I'd usually get bored in them, make my pager go off, and leave early anyway.)

Colin is one of the reps who is welcome anytime. And seeing him *is* good patient care. You should also strive to be a partner in care, so that visiting with you is part of the treatment process, never a distraction.

But there is more to it than that – thousands of reps contribute significantly to patient care, why do some get instant access while others rarely do?

I took up this question by first surveying my colleagues as to which reps they allowed into their offices anytime. A list of the same names kept coming up in my territory. There was no real pattern, many different products were represented and virtually every company. So what was special about this crew? Well, I arranged meetings with these twelve reps, and after I met them, one thing was clear – **every one of them loved their jobs.**

Each rep was unique, each had their own style of selling, and some were even naturally shy! But they loved their roles as physician educators, they detailed and interacted with the passion that comes from the belief that they have excellent products, their products help people, and it is their mission to get the word out.

Summary:

- Reps who have a standing invitation and unlimited access are trusted members of treatment teams, and

- Reps with unlimited access are similar in their love of their jobs, and their natural passion.

- If you believe your product is superior and is the best choice, let it show.

- The passion you have for your job and products is the key to persuasion *and* access!

'Who's sponsoring this dinner program?'

Chapter 17

The Speaker Program and Physician Education

The medical speaker program continues to be a valued educational event. Your customers want to hear new data and the first-hand product experiences of respected colleagues. The right speaker can promote your product to new levels of usage and help to get treatment to a significant number of patients in need.

You may have heard the sound-byte that more dollars spent on drug marketing translates into more prescriptions, which is something your critics tout, but this is factually untrue. Extent of product use reflects several factors, most importantly efficacy and ease of usage (ease for the clinician as well as tolerability for the patient), but specific to physician marketing, the real issue is education – the more we know about the benefits, risks, side effects, and experience related to a drug, the more comfortable we are using it.

The speaker program is an excellent way to relay the data we need in order to feel confident prescribing an agent, and facilitating educational programs in your community is another way you can provide value to your customers. But the real value is to our patient populations.

Guide to a Successful Program

A successful program does not mean good service and a properly functioning LCD projector. It means increased product usage after the fact, it means your speaker was persuasive and conveyed his or her belief that your product is the best option when indicated.

It means your speaker had an impact. Thus, the first rule:

1. Pick the Right Speaker!

You have all been disappointed when a speaker was boring, poorly informed, or neglected your product. You are paying for a service and you deserve the best. Ask your colleagues which speakers are effective and captivating. Any speaker can read a slide kit, but who really persuades? When I surveyed doctors about what qualities make a speaker persuasive, and further, what about that speaker inspires them to reconsider and even change their prescription habits, these were the results:

- A speaker with extensive product experience.

- Someone respected for clinical and research contributions.

- A doctor who is a passionate speaker.

Of these three qualities, which was ranked as the most important? It was **passion** for the product, the message, the patient's best interest. The passionate speaker was the most effective. Recall the rep qualities we discussed in Chapters 16 and 17, and the reps who are always welcome and are more persuasive than their colleagues? – It is their passion that drives their message, and the same quality serves the physician speaker equally well.

2. Brief your Speaker

When I speak at CME or dinner programs, I need to know the specialties present and need a briefing on the exact needs of the audience. It may only be a sentence or two – but it is critical. Again, a speaker is there to meet *your* needs. I was recently informed that my audience "had two neurologists who were interested in chronic pain reduction on antidepressants, an obstetrician who had asked about post-partem depression, and family care doctors interested in the side effect profile as compared to others in the class." That excellent briefing allowed me to meet the group's needs perfectly, and I was invited back to Rome (...well, Rome, Georgia).

Speakers who are unpredictable, or 'loose cannons' at the podium will waste your resources. Also, those who show no respect for audience needs will harm your efforts, not advance them. A rather arrogant speaker came to our community and was unfortunately booked in a small restaurant next to the noisy open-area kitchen. After just five minutes, he asked 'can you hear me in the back?' 'No,' was the reply, 'well, enjoy dinner!' and then he sat down and refused to speak!

This was a challenging venue, but not an excuse to forget his obligation. If he was frustrated, and the noise level was too high for a formal lecture, it was time for visits to each table to hit the high points and answer questions. I helped the rep feel better about the disastrous night by sitting next to the speaker and asking him how much he charged for lecture, and then fibbing that myself and everyone I know gets paid four or five times as much for our talks.

3. Control Your Program

In a large Midwestern city this year, a group of physicians sat at the back of the room and held their own rather loud roundtable discussion while I spoke. I'm pretty sure it had nothing to do with antidepressants. Now, this is highly unusual - that a covey of audience members would be so discourteous to a guest. The rep was a wonderful lady, she saw how distracted I was and that my tactic for dealing with the situation was not working (I went to the back of the room and stood in front of the gang, my back to them while I spoke, thus, all the other audience members would be looking in their direction, while my body language showed I was ignoring them). When none of this worked, Kate (the rep) risked her relationship status with them to ask them to be quiet. She took control and I was grateful, as were the more polite attendees.

123

Taking control means you direct the event, tell the staff when to serve, help with seating and set-up, and do whatever it takes to support the speaker and keep the program on track.

4. Ask Questions You Want Answered

If a speaker neglects an area you want covered, you can ask a question as well as any audience member. This is your program, and it needs to fit the needs of your territory, so don't be shy about important topics. Particularly if one of your docs in attendance has asked you about a topic in the past - now you can allow the speaker to enhance the message you have previously delivered. As a speaker, I greatly appreciate rep questions; they are the slow hanging curve balls I hit out of the park!

5. Invites Key Physicians

Obviously you will invite your key physicians, but get better attendance by personalizing the invitations. Such as: "Dr Farah, I know you see only hospital patients, and tonight the speaker will go over all the inpatient trials for drug X." We are more likely to show up if it meets our specific needs. Also, introduce the speaker to key physicians so their specific questions can be addressed.

6. Use the trip

If you can arrange more than one lecture or roundtable for your speaker, do so! Make the most of the trip, and you'll get the best ROI. I usually head to the Pacific Northwest twice a year and spend a week lecturing. I am usually booked all day for riding with reps, breakfast talks, lunches, dinners - whatever they need. It's an effective way to promote your drug, and get the most influential speakers in front of your most important customers; and you will have a chance to get private time and instruction from your speaker. The folks in Yakima are terrific, and the reps are wonderful, but perhaps next year my services will be needed for a week or two in Hawaii...

A Matter of Opinion

Too many speakers are afraid to voice their opinions, fearing they will sound like a commercial for the sponsor. They operate under the assumption that in order to be perceived as objective they cannot speak in support of any one product. Speakers are often so self-conscious of this that they make ridiculous statements – I have heard speakers say, "It doesn't matter which drug in this class you use" (the logical extension of this is: then why are we here listening to a lecture about their differences?). And I have heard speakers specifically avoid the sponsor product believing that this somehow enhances their credibility.

As speakers, we are expected to look at all available data objectively, but we should still form opinions. In fact, one could argue that that is exactly what we are being hired for – any physician can read a study or a slide based summary of the data, but speakers are hired to further discuss impressions of the data and personal clinical experience.

The audience considers *our* personal experience with the product one of the most important aspects of the speaker program. When surveyed, the top five responses to the question 'what do you want to hear at a speaker program?' physicians listed these items that can guide you when briefing your speakers:

1. **Speaker experience** – attendees want to know what we have seen with the drug. Not only are we the experts, we have used it, and they want to benefit from that personal data. If one of your docs would like to speak on behalf of your product, but has very little experience with it, there is no need to send them to training. This is not some petty strategy to force more use of a particular drug, it is just a fact that audiences want to know what the speaker has seen while using the medication, and they need to be prepared to talk about it.

2. **Something new** – the second most common response to the survey was 'tell me something new.' Most attendees will be familiar with the medication's use and side effect profile; many have read the complete package insert. Keep an eye out for any new studies, head to head trials, or interesting case reports that your audience may find useful, particularly information that representatives are not allowed to share. We all want to be innovative and on the cutting edge, and audiences will look to speakers to tell them the latest.

3. **Clinical trial data** – the clinical trial may be commonly criticized (the patients are 'study patients, not real world') but it remains the standard for testing and approving new drugs. The data they generate will shape practices for years, and programs should include relevant trials.

4. **Side effect profile and management** – we all accept that medications have side effects, even placebo pills - and colleagues will see these side effects in their practices. They want to know from the experts what to do about them (lower the dose? split the dose? add an antidote?).

5. **Experience in other countries** – finally, audiences are very curious about the experience in countries where a drug has been released prior to US approval. In fact, there may be a wealth of such data, and it enhances a provider's confidence to know millions of patients may have benefited from a drug before we utilize it, and a basic Medline (or similar) search will provide this information.

Summary:

- The most passionate speakers are the most effective ones.

- Speakers should be hired for their opinions, not for their lack of them.

- Audiences want to know: speaker experience, new data, side effect management, and experiences from clinical trials and from other countries.

- As a rep you should:
  1. Control the program.
  2. Select the best speaker you can.
  3. Brief them on audience needs.
  4. Invite key docs and introduce them to the speaker.
  5. Never be shy about asking questions yourself.
  6. Use the trip and your speaker's time to the fullest for the best ROI.
  7. Invite me to Hawaii, Puerto Rico, and West Palm as often as possible.

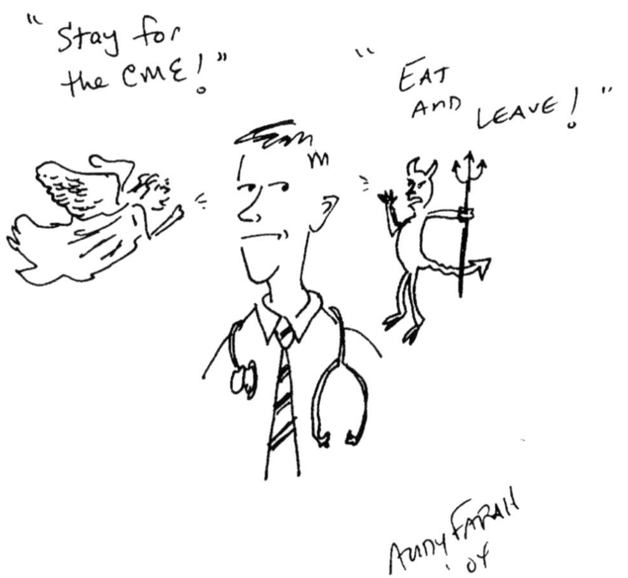
"Stay for the CME!"
"EAT AND LEAVE!"
ANDY FARAH '04

Glossary of Essential Information

Double blind study: A study in which neither the subjects nor those administering and evaluating treatment are aware of which preparation is placebo or active drug, (or which of more than one of the active drugs are administered).

Drug: In a general sense, a drug is any substance having a chemical action that brings about a change in biological function. Most drugs interact with a target site in the body or 'receptor,' but they can also interact with infectious agents (bacteria, viruses). A drug's ability to interact with a target site (whether it fits the receptor, as a key in a lock, or partially fits it) is dependent on the specific atoms that make up the drug molecule. Thus, its atomic composition will obviously determine its size, three dimensional shape, and electrical charge, all of which are critical. Drug sizes vary from extremely small (such as lithium, an element, with a molecular weight (MW) of 7 to some protein products, like immune globulins (proteins can have MW's of almost 60,000)). Most drugs are between 100 and 1000, and drugs larger than MW1000 are unlikely to diffuse between compartments of the body and may need to be administered directly at their target sites.

Drug absorption and metabolism: When a patient takes a pill or capsule, it is generally broken down in the stomach and absorbed in the intestine. Not all of the drug molecules are absorbed in every case, and some percentage of certain drugs may be excreted through the GI system unabsorbed. For the most part, however, the molecules are absorbed across the tissue and into the GI circulation, and these vessels all lead to one pathway – the portal circulation -

which flows directly to the liver. The liver's job is to break down compounds in the system, (our own, such as blood cells, as well as foreign chemicals). Unless severely damaged, the liver is usually highly efficient. If the target receptors for the drug are in the stomach or intestines, obviously the action occurs prior to the liver breakdown. Some drugs are absorbed intact from the small intestine and the liver handles all of the metabolism, while others are more extensively metabolized in the GI tract than the liver. Many times, the metabolites are active drugs, and in some cases, they are the primary drug. Liquid forms of medication are associated with higher rates of absorption, and though it varies from drug to drug, absorption can be increased by as much as 30% by switching to a liquid preparation.

FDA: Food and Drug Administration, which oversees the drug evaluation process and grants approval for marketing new drugs in the US. Its authority and role has evolved through several legislative acts, the first of which was in 1906 – The Pure Food and Drug Act, which prohibited mislabeling and adulteration of drugs.

First pass effect/First pass metabolism: The metabolism that occurs after the drug is absorbed from the GI system and travels to the liver by the portal circulation. Drugs with a higher degree of first pass metabolism will show marked variation in blood levels from patient to patient, as blood flows and liver function obviously vary. Other routes of administration, such as sublingual, transdermal, or intramuscular, will avoid the first-pass effect.

Generic drug: A compound that is chemically identical to the brand-name drug on which it is based, however, the FDA allows up to a 20% difference between the two with respect to bioavailability, C_{max}, and T_{max}. Patients switched to generics may therefore experience problems such as a 40% decrease in bioavailability. "Fillers" or non-active ingredients may also vary widely among different generics, and can account for new side effects not observed in brand products.

Half life: The time it takes for the plasma concentration of a drug to drop by 50% (many people falsely assume a drug is fully eliminated at half-life time). A drug's metabolites may have longer half-lives than their parent compounds. Metabolites may or may not be active in the same way the parent drug is.

LD50: The median dose of a compound that proves fatal in 50% of animals tested.

NDA: New Drug Application, submitted to the FDA after phase III trials, consisting of hundreds of volumes of data – full reports of all pre-clinical and clinical data. The FDA may allow some marketing prior to completion of all phase III studies.

P value: A statistical way of comparing two sets of data, specifically, a way of determining if the difference between them is significant, or if it could have occurred by mere chance. A P value will further describe the importance of the difference. For example, if one drug improves blood pressure to a normal range in 76% of the patients taking it, and a placebo improves it in 30% of subjects, and the P value is calculated to be less than 0.05, then the probability that this difference between the two groups occurred by chance is less than one in twenty. If the P value is less than 0.01, then the difference could still be the result of random chance, but the odds of that are less than one in one hundred (<1%), which is highly unlikely. Nearly every study you discuss will have associated P values, and be sure to point out P values that are "statistically significant" ($P<.05$) and those that are "statistically highly significant" ($P<.01$).

Phases of Medication Research:

Phase 1: The first of three stages of clinical trials required for FDA approval, and usually last over six months. The aim is to evaluate drug safety and pharmacokinetic properties. Studies involve small numbers of healthy volunteers.

Phase 2: The second of three stages of trials required by the FDA, aimed at determining if the drug treats the condition for which it is intended. Larger groups are studied than in phase 1, usually using single-blind studies. About one of three drugs in phase 2 trials move on to Phase 3.

Phase 3: Involves much larger numbers of patients, often thousands, and double-blind and crossover studies are used to minimize errors caused by placebo effects.

Phase 4: A clinical trial of a drug already available and approved by the FDA.

Pharmacodynamic: Describes the actions of the drug on the body.

Pharmacokinetic: Describes the actions of the body on the drug.

Placebo effect: A clinically significant and reported side effect occurring after administering a non-active compound.

Placebo nonreactor subject: A subject in a study who does not respond therapeutically to a placebo, and may be selected for a therapeutic trial in order to make comparisons with active drugs more sensitive.

Placebo response: A reduction in symptoms from a baseline measure in a placebo treated group.

Power analysis: Statistical measure that evaluates whether the number of subject is adequate to draw the conclusions of interest to the study.

Pregnancy categories:

Category A: Pregnant women have taken these drugs in controlled studies and no risk to the fetus has been demonstrated.
Category B: No evidence of risk in humans has been demonstrated.
Category C: Risk cannot be ruled out. Human studies have not been conducted, and animal studies have not been done, or are positive for potential risk. Yet, benefit may outweigh risk. Examples include all SSRI antidepressants (escitalopram, citalopram, paroxetine, fluoxetine, sertraline).
Category D: Positive evidence for risk, yet in specific cases, the drug's benefit may still outweigh risk.
Category X: Not to be used in pregnancy, no potential benefit outweighs the known risk.
(Be sure to know the pregnancy categories for the medications you represent, and their competitors, and it is useful to know if there are published case reports of patients who have been breast-feeding on the medication. You will be asked, so be prepared to send the necessary inquiry to medical affairs!)

Protein binding: Drugs in the circulation are often bound (by electrical charge) to proteins circulating in the blood. The amount of free, or unbound drug, confers the desired activity.

Risk of defect in child **not** exposed to any drug in utero is 3-4% (contrary to popular belief, the vast majority of birth defects are spontaneous and unrelated to drug therapy)

Schedule of Controlled Drugs

Schedule I: Highest abuse potential, no accepted medical usage, and use is illegal except for certain types of approved research (mostly street drugs, examples: heroin, LSD, peyote, MDA).

Schedule II: Accepted medical use, but high risk of abuse and dependency, no phoned-in prescriptions and no refills allowed (certain opioids: oxycodone, hydromorphone, methadone; stimulants: amphetamine, methylphenidate; certain depressants: pentobarbital and similar).

Schedule III: Risk of physical dependency, and high potential for psychological dependency; five refills allowed, or new prescription needed after 6 months (certain opioids in combination with non-opioid ingredients: Vicodin, Lortab; certain schedule II barbiturates in mixture with non-controlled agents; Anabolic steroids: oxandrolone, testosterone).

Schedule IV: Like schedule III, prescriptions expire after 6 months, and five refills allowed, but differ from schedule III in penalties related to illegal possession (certain opiates: propoxyphene (Darvon), pentazocine (Talwin); all benzodiazepines – Valium, Xanax, and zaleplon (Sonata) and zolpidem (Ambien)).

Schedule V: Any other nonopioid drug dispensed without prescription.

Steady state: Drug plasma level at which absorption of the drug and elimination are in a state of equilibrium. The time it takes to attain a steady state is about four or five half-lives after initiation of therapy. (If a drug's half-life is 24 hours, it will be at steady state concentration about four or five days into therapy) The average plasma steady state level does not change whether the drug is given once a day or in divided doses.

Contact Information:

You can reach **Dr. Farah** at:
Phone 336-664-9218
Fax 336-931-1367
Email: drandyfarah@yahoo.com

Address:

Farah Consulting
8755 Bame Rd.
Colfax, NC 27235

Seminar Information:

Dr. Farah is available for consultations regarding sales and marketing strategy. He has spoken to numerous pharmaceutical training sessions about the physician customer and specific product selling strategy.

He is also available for the lectures:
"The Accidental Leader" and "The Pyramid of Leadership," which are designed to help managers and other pharmaceutical company employees effectively handle new leadership responsibilities, and provide the basis for future growth in management skills.

About the Author:

Dr. Andy Farah was born in Charleston, SC. He attended Clemson University and then The Medical University of South Carolina. He completed his psychiatry residency at Wake Forest University in 1994. He practices general psychiatry in the Triad of NC, lectures on psychopharmacology, and has contributed to numerous clinical and business publications. He began researching medical decision-making in 1992.